Student Resiliency

Student Resiliency

The Subtle Art of Wellness

Paul F. Granello and Matthew S. Fleming

cognella

SAN DIEGO

Bassim Hamadeh, CEO and Publisher
Amy Smith, Senior Project Editor
Alia Bales, Production Editor
Jess Estrella, Senior Graphic Designer
Kylie Bartolome, Licensing Associate
Natalie Piccotti, Director of Marketing
Kassie Graves, Senior Vice President of Editorial
Jamie Giganti, Director of Academic Publishing

3970 Sorrento Valley Blvd., Ste. 500, San Diego, CA 9212

We dedicate this book to the friends and families of those who have died from the COVID-19 virus and who continue to struggle with it and its aftermath. The past year has been very challenging as our country and the world experienced terrible loss and turmoil. We hope this book helps new college students better cope with the hardship of the pandemic in addition to the usual stress of entering college.

Brief Contents

Detailed Contents

Preface

Over the last decade, I have noticed that college students are becoming more anxious and depressed. My clinical work and my work in the Stress Management and Resiliency Training Lab have both confirmed this belief. I wanted to do something to help college students adjust to college but even more so to learn how to live a well lifestyle. Hence this book.

The purpose of this book is to help students become more resilient by employing healthy choices and wellness habits. It is our belief that if students use this workbook, they will achieve a happier and healthier way of navigating the stresses and strains of college life.

Sincerely,
Paul F. Granello, PhD, LPCC-S, CWC

Acknowledgments

Matt Fleming

My deep gratitude to Dr. Paul Granello and Dr. Darcy Granello for accepting me into the highly rated counselor education department at The Ohio State University and for their mentoring and friendship over the past 15 years. Their teaching and guidance prepared me for my second career as a therapist in both the university setting and, later, in private practice.

My thanks to the OSU Counseling and Consultation Service (CCS), where I interned. OSU CCS provided me much training and support as well as diverse professional experience as a therapist.

Finally, I extend much appreciation to my wife, Carol Fleming, for her love, support, and useful editing of my writing.

Paul Granello

I wish to acknowledge my academic mentors and outstanding students. I especially want to recognize my fantastic wife, Darcy Haag Granello, for her outstanding support and constant love. I also want to recognize my mother, Alanna C. Granello, for her support.

CHAPTER 1

An Introduction to Wellness & Resiliency

Paul F. Granello, PhD, LPCC-S, CWC & Brett Zyromski, PhD

What Is Wellness?

Wellness is a health philosophy (a theory) characterized by three main principles. The first of these is an emphasis on prevention. The second is active striving on the part of the individual. The third is an orientation toward self-care (Figure 1.1).

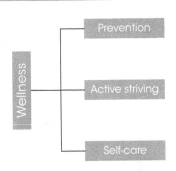

FIGURE 1.1   Parts of Wellness

Prevention

The United States spends more on healthcare per capita than any other country on earth. Yet half of the adult population in the United States has a chronic medical condition (obesity, diabetes, arthritis, depression, etc.). This is because our healthcare system is not well suited for preventing chronic health conditions. We have a great system for coping with acute injuries but a poor system for dealing with chronic health issues. Our traditional medical model is focused on illness and its causes or pathogens. Wellness, with its emphasis on prevention as a healthcare philosophy, is focused on variables that make us feel better, or salutogens. A salutogen can be anything that contributes to your health in a positive way, such as a bike ride, eating an apple, spending time with friends, a healthy relationship, or a challenging problem. Resilient people purposefully build salutogens into their lives each day.

Prevention is the avoidance of illness altogether or, in the case of disease management, a reduction in the severity of an illness. Prevention programs aim to help individuals avoid getting illnesses in the first place, thereby saving human suffering and expensive medical care. Disease management programs seek to reduce the severity of diseases in order to reduce human suffering and save medical care costs.

Active Striving

The patient in the traditional medical model often plays a passive role. The doctor is in the role of expert, and the individual follows doctor's orders. Wellness, however, is a health philosophy that encourages the **individual to take responsibility for their own health**. Further, the individual is encouraged to constantly strive for optimum functioning across all the domains of well-being. Being well, therefore, is not just being free of illness but rather is a constant pursuit of increased health. Well people monitor their functioning across wellness domains, set goals for improvement, and work to gain increasing health as a preventative measure against illness.

Self-Care

While well people use medical services when necessary and take advantage of preventative medical programs, they strongly believe that individuals must be the primary caregivers for themselves. This means that each person takes responsibility for managing their health instead of turning over control of their health to an expert. Well people take action to educate themselves about their health needs so they can make the most of their time with health experts. They ask questions of their healthcare providers and participate in developing healthcare plans.

FIGURE 1.2   Continuum of Care

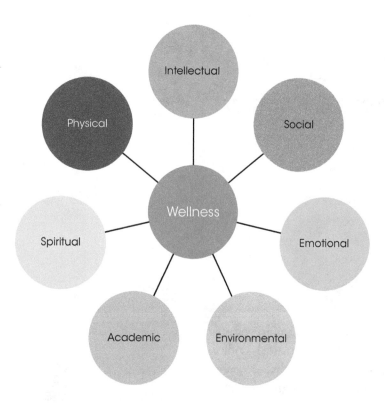

FIGURE 1.3   Wellness Model

Wellness is also holistic in nature. Health is looked at through the lens of the whole person and their overall functioning. The individual is not divided up into parts and pieces, as often happens in today's medical environment—an environment that is characterized by the more focused lenses of medical specialists who only work with a part of the person. Wellness seeks to work with the whole ecosystem of the physical and mental health of the person at one time, realizing that these often influence each other.

Finally, all of the domains of wellness interact and influence each other all the time. We have divided wellness into domains in our model in order to make it easier to study each domain individually. Realize that improvement in one domain is likely going to have additional positive effects in other domains. For example, improvement in the physical domain (exercising and eating well) will probably help the emotional and intellectual domains.

TABLE 1.1 Seven Domains of Wellness Defined	
Intellectual	Encompasses all the mental activities of the individual's brain that create consciousness. Perception, memory, appraisal, and attribution are all examples.
Social	The influences of interactions with others on the health of the individual. Example: the ability to draw on and provide emotional support to others.
Emotional	The ability of individuals to monitor and modify their emotions for the purpose of controlling their level of arousal. Example: managing arousal from negative emotions by engaging in activities such as yoga or breathing exercises.
Environmental	The impacts the settings and times in which individuals exist have upon their health. Example: access to safe drinking water, access to healthcare, beliefs about women's rights.
Academic	The ability of the individual to set reasonable and meaningful academic goals and to succeed at fulfilling them.
Spiritual	An individual's system of beliefs or values that provide a sense of purpose in life. Example: the belief that there is an organizing principle or creator of the universe.
Physical	The positive use of exercise and diet to achieve and maintain healthy body and mind. Example: eating a well-balanced diet.

What Is Resiliency?

To be resilient means to have the ability to "come back" from adversity. The story of resilience is really the story of human adaptation. Neenan (2018) suggests that to understand resilience, we must first "discover the meaning (attitudes and beliefs) that people attach to adverse life events" (pp. 1–2). To illustrate his point, Neenan (2018) offers a story, which is adjusted here to illuminate how the impact of resilience may play out in a common life experience of an undergraduate student. To better understand resilience, imagine two people you know who have experienced a very similar issue, such as the breakup of a significant romantic relationship. Obviously, many aspects of the quality of those relationships might differ, but let's imagine, just for a moment, that both relationships were equally positive and both shared similar foundational characteristics. Both people might initially feel hurt and rejected. Over time, though, they may show significant differences in how they deal with the loss of their romantic relationships. One person, let's call them Person A, may commit to spending more time with a few quality friends, increase their time in mindfulness practices, such as meditation and yoga, work with a counselor to unpack how the relationship ended to attribute appropriate responsibility to each person in the relationship, spend more time outdoors walking or jogging, and hold to a belief that life has purpose and additional positive relationships are likely to happen for them in the future. Realizing the effort it takes to prioritize these strategies for adapting to and coping with the breakup, Person A also creates an academic calendar with due dates and goals for studying to ensure they stay on track academically through the tough times.

Unfortunately, the other person, Person B, may find their anger and bitterness increase over time. They blame their former partner for the breakup and become envious of their friends still in romantic relationships. Person B decides the best way to get over the breakup is to forget their former partner through going out to as many parties as possible, increasing their drinking, and rejecting outright the support offered by a few close friends. The close friends, in fact, begin drawing away from Person B, as Person B seems angry and lashes out whenever their close friends suggest ways to move on from the breakup. When one friend suggests Person B take advantage of the free counseling services provided through the counseling center on campus, Person B gets frustrated and asks if the counselor is going to help get their romantic partner back. If not, then what's the use of going to see a counselor?

As Neenan (2018) suggested, to better understand why the two people you know responded so differently to a very similar life event, it is important to understand how the person applies meaning to that event. Person A seemed to view the life event as part of the journey of life and holds hope that additional positive romantic relationships will occur in the future. Person A began drawing on resources from each of the domains of wellness. For example, Person A seeks support from a group of key friends, gaining resources from the social domain of wellness. They tap into the environmental supports around them through using the counseling center on campus as well as the recreation center on campus, which offers free yoga and meditation classes. The yoga and meditation provide emotional wellness outlets. Meditation helps Person A consider their spiritual tenet that life has purpose. Walking or jogging provides needed physical wellness, which may also reflect environmental resources if there are jogging paths or parks in their neighborhood. Through their time with their counselor, Person A is applying their intellectual wellness approaches by attributing appropriate responsibility to each party for the relationship ending. Finally, acknowledging that the adversity created by the breakup requires substantial time and effort to navigate, even using the resources across each of the domains of wellness, Person A strategically creates academic goals and priorities to ensure they stay on track. These academic wellness approaches will come in handy as the semester continues despite the adversity they are navigating. This anecdote illustrates how a resilient person can come back from adversity more quickly than someone who is less resilient. We will consider how each of the domains of wellness influences resilience. However, first, let's explore the definition of resilience.

Researchers have been exploring the topic of resilience for decades (Van Breda, 2018) in an attempt to better understand how people recover differently from adversity. It is clear that adverse life events can have harmful effects on people. As the anecdote above illustrated, how a person adapts to and copes with those events will directly inform the way they bounce back from those events. It is important to note that these skills are not static skills. They can be learned, and the process of adapting and coping may take various amounts of time (Neenan, 2018). We believe, however, that often a resilient person works through a problem across all domains of wellness on their journey to return to a pre-event level of functioning. To help inform the process of applying resilience, Neenan and Dryden (Neenan, 2018) have come up with an extensive definition of the characteristics of a resilient person, which is described in Box 1.1.

BOX 1.1: AXIOMS FOR A RESILIENT PERSON

Resilience According to Neenan & Dryden (Neenan, 2018):

Resilience is a set of flexible cognitive, emotional, and behavioral responses to acute or chronic adversity. Resilient people are flexible.

Resilient responses are learnable, and anyone can master them. Resilience is for everyone.

At the heart of resilience is the attitude (meaning) a person adopts in relation to adversity. Resilient people see adversity as a challenge to be overcome. Resilience is working through or coming back (not bouncing back) from adversity. There are often pain and struggle to overcome. Resilient people do not let the pain associated with adversity stop them from working through problems. Resilient people move forward despite adversity, struggle, or pain. Resilient people solve problems that can be fixed or adapt their goals but always move forward. Resilience includes external and internal factors. Resilient people are helped by having a good social support system. Resilient people leverage external opportunities. Resilient people learn from experiencing adversities and apply those learnings to cope with future adversity.

What are your thoughts or feelings after reading the seven axioms that reflect Neenan and Dryden's (Neenan, 2018) definition of resilience? Perhaps you feel hopeful that resilience can be learned and anyone can master resilient responses. Perhaps you remember a recent time of adversity you experienced and the pain and struggle you experienced as you worked through that event. Perhaps you feel encouraged that you kept moving forward despite the struggle and pain and that you seem to persist, no matter the obstacles. Perhaps you feel there is much for you to learn about how to coordinate your support system, including both internal and external factors, to serve you as you navigate life and the adversity it brings. We believe an attitude of resilience can be informed and strengthened by an intentional focus on enhancing wellness across the seven domains of wellness. But why is this necessary for college students?

Resilience is a benefit for any person to cultivate, but it is of particular benefit to college students. College students experience an inordinate amount of adversity due to stressful life events. It is important to remember that stressful life events and potentially traumatic events can be perceived differently by different individuals. It is that perception, and the meaning applied to those events, which then require the application of different levels of resiliency across the wellness domains to navigate successfully. Researchers found 77% of an undergraduate and graduate sample reported at least one potentially traumatic event (Beasley et al., 2003). Other authors have reported that between 55% and 84% (depending on the sample in the study) of college students experienced a stressful life event (Smyth et al., 2008). Disturbingly, data from the Center for Collegiate Mental Health (2020) reflects rates of self-harm behaviors as well as serious suicidal ideation and attempts have increased over the past decade. Other mental health issues exist for college students as well. For example, compared to the anxiety and depression rates of the general population (19.1% and 7.1%, respectively; National Institute of Mental Health, 2017, 2019), anxiety and depression rates in college students are much higher, ranging from 38–55% for anxiety and 12–22% for depression (American College Health Association, 2014; Beiter et al., 2015; Center for Collegiate Mental Health, 2020; Chung et al., 2011; Francis & Horn, 2017; Nilsson et al., 2004). The high prevalence of stressful life events and potentially traumatic events experienced by college students as well as the mental health issues experienced by a relatively high percentage of college students reinforce the need for cultivating resilience intentionally across the seven domains of wellness. As students cultivate resiliency, the benefits will reverberate across their mental, physical, and emotional health.

What Are the Benefits of Resiliency?

In brief, the benefits of resilience are directly related to the ability of the person to navigate the stressful life events or potentially traumatic events in such a way that they are able to interrupt the potential risk to their life functioning and maintain positive outcomes. Zimmerman and colleagues (2013) suggested resilience reflects a strengths-based approach to enhancing preventative and promotive factors in youth. In this book, we extend the strengths-based lens to a wellness lens, examining resiliency through the seven domains of wellness. In the following subsections, we briefly offer a few examples of the benefits of applying each domain of wellness to enhance resiliency. These and more will be further explicated throughout the other chapters in this book, but we hope this brief introduction to the connection between the dimensions of wellness and resilience will help frame the myriad potential benefits.

Intellectual Wellness and Resiliency

College students apply their brains to their work every day. However, how students apply their brains to their work every day could be a function of the way they think about their work and stressful events that occur at college. For example, people can respond in rational or irrational ways to academic challenges. Some researchers suggest students' academic rational beliefs (ARBs) influence their work habits and their levels of resilience (Warren & Hale, 2020). Rational beliefs are flexible thoughts people apply to respond to challenges in a healthy and productive manner. As students apply rational beliefs, they avoid exaggerating the impact of any event, which some researchers call "awfulizing" the event, or making it worse than it needs to be. Rational thought also helps students avoid aligning their self-worth or value with the stressful event. Students who apply rational beliefs are more likely to work toward their academic goals and prepare well for exams (Warren & Hale, 2020). Rational beliefs help people take responsibility for their actions and make commitments toward achieving goals. Other skills researchers often report leading to resilience include problem-solving skills, planning skills, and executive functioning (see Masten, 2018 for a list of resiliency factors).

Social Wellness and Resiliency

Positive relationships with family and friends have been associated with lower levels of anxiety and depression (Skrove et al., 2013). Unsurprisingly, it turns out that having good relationships with family members or with two or more friends can help alleviate mental health issues. For example, in one study of undergraduate and graduate students in social work programs, Wilks (2008) found when students reported feeling supported by friends, it helped increase their resiliency and buffer academic stress. However, the extensiveness of the social network may actually be detrimental to building resiliency. For example, some authors (Galatzer-Levy et al., 2012) found that for those experiencing high levels of stress, an extensive social network may contribute to instability and stress. Conversely, high-quality, high-contact relationships were more beneficial. Apparently, it is not having a vast network of friends that is most beneficial to social wellness: rather, it is the quality of the relationships. Thus, those who have a manageable number of positive social relationships may benefit more than people who focus on expanding the number of social networks.

Another way social activities help promote resiliency is through the overlap they create with other areas of wellness. Many areas of wellness may overlap, but when college students actively involve themselves in prosocial activities, it often results in participation in activities that advance physical, emotional, intellectual, spiritual, or academic wellness. It is not difficult to imagine a college student coordinating a Sunday-morning excursion to an area church, a walk in the woods, or a trip to the gym for a workout or basketball game. When people participate in organized activities, they apply their resources to enhance health development (Zimmerman et al., 2013). Students are able to experience success, increase self-efficacy, and explore new areas of interest as they build positive relationships with others.

Emotional Wellness and Resiliency

If we return to Neenan's (2018) suggestion that we need to understand how people apply meaning to an event to understand how they respond to that event, then it would make sense that meaning might be constructed through thoughts and emotions. How people think about an event often leads directly to feelings. We previously mentioned that college students face a myriad of stressors and potentially traumatic events that can lead to anxiety, depression, and other negative outcomes. Emotional wellness is an incredibly important buffer to help increase resilience and avoid these negative outcomes. For example, self-compassion is an important tenet to apply to increase resiliency and successfully respond to stressful life events (Bluth et al., 2018; Neff et al., 2005, 2007). People with lower levels of self-compassion tend to get down on themselves during tough times; they ruminate about what is happening to them. People with higher levels of self-compassion tend to be happier, more curious, more conscientious, more social, and ready to take personal initiative (Neff et al., 2007). Neff and colleagues (2005) share that self-compassion includes taking an open, nonjudgmental attitude toward yourself and your suffering, being nonjudgmental toward your inadequacies and failures, and framing your experience in the light of the larger human experience. This helps avoid self-pitying behavior or overidentification with stressful or potentially traumatic events. Students with self-compassion were kinder to themselves when they experienced academic failure and were more likely to experience that failure as a chance to learn and grow rather than tying the failure to their self-worth. Further, even after failure, students with self-compassion were able to remain intrinsically motivated. They did not remain defeated but remained involved in the course topic and retained a feeling that they still had competence. Self-compassion has also shown to buffer some of the mental health issues, such as anxiety and depression, that college students often struggle with (Neff, 2003).

One important aspect of self-compassion is the concept of mindfulness (Neff et al., 2005; Rogers, 2013). Mindfulness reflects a person's ability to take a balanced view of events through nonjudgmental awareness of the present moment that encapsulates a clarity and acceptance of mental and emotional phenomena as they occur. Rogers (2013) suggests mindfulness has been shown to help shorten the amount of time it takes to recover from traumatic stress. Mindfulness augments positive emotions, and the increase of positive emotions helps increase resilience. College students can benefit from mindfulness as a practice to help regulate their emotional responses to stressful traumas.

Environmental Wellness and Resiliency

The environment in which we live has a profound effect upon our health. If we consider the systemic impacts of inequality, racism, pandemics, extreme weather events (e.g., hurricanes, floods, and wildfires, among others), and sociopolitical events that result in war-related traumas, it is clear that the environment in which we live significantly contributes to our well-being or lack thereof. The good news, especially for those engaged in pursuing environmental wellness, is that even after adversity has been experienced, if there are resources within the environment that support healthy functioning, then people have the capacity to use these resources to increase their ability to deal with the adversities they encounter (Ungar, 2013). For example, Schiele and Domschke (2018) report people who experience environmental adversity are at an increased level of vulnerability for developing anxiety compared to people who don't face similar adversity. However, positive social support and the ability to apply cognitive self-regulation strategies have both been linked to decreases in symptoms of anxiety and other mental health issues (Schiele & Domschke, 2018). Thus, if there are resources within the environment, such as social support or counseling to reinforce practice in self-regulation strategies that people access and apply to work through the adversity, in the end, they have the potential to flourish. In the words of Schiele and Domschke (2018), "In this regard, nurture trumps nature when it comes to predicting resilience" (p. 258).

That is not to say interventions should not be directed at changing the environment to help reduce adversity people experience. Even just acknowledging the system is challenging or oppressive can be helpful to identify both the adversity being faced and the resources available within the environment to access and apply to increase resilience. For example, Griffin and others (2020) pointed out a focus on racial identity is a critical component of self-awareness for Black youth. They found when Black students managed race-related stress (adversity from the system) with active coping mechanisms, such as planning a student walkout in response to a racist incident in the school or creating a Black Student Union organization, then their cognitive strategy use increased as well (e.g., students were more likely to relate study material to prior knowledge). Consider that as students applied active coping mechanisms, they drew from the environmental resources as well, as both examples provided above require social connectedness and capital to take action around shared values. Changing the system itself to provide additional opportunities for Black students while at the same time providing interventions that increase active coping mechanisms and enhanced racial identity could result in both needed systemic change and increases in resilience for Black students. Environments can simultaneously be oppressive and provide opportunities.

College students often exist in environments in which resources are available. It is vital that college students navigate to, and take advantage of, those resources to increase resilience (Ungar, 2013). For example, students often have access to healthcare, student groups and clubs that represent others with similar values, counseling services, recreation centers on campus, religious and spiritual resources (e.g., nearby churches, spiritual organizations, or student religious/ spiritual organizations), and academic supports (e.g., tutoring or writing centers). Many of these resources will offer the potential for increased social connectedness. It often requires personal motivation to identify the options that are available to us that we can access to increase our coping strategies and resilience. Take, for instance, the opportunity to attend a spiritual gathering that aligns with your own values on a Saturday morning. There is still choice involved: Do you stay in bed and sleep away the grogginess you feel from the previous evening's activities, or do you push yourself to take advantage of the opportunity to enhance your spiritual wellness and potentially expand your social connectedness? We have a role in taking advantage of those resources in our environment that can facilitate wellness and resilience.

Academic Wellness and Resiliency

College students face a myriad of academic stressors. In a previous section, we discussed the importance of rational cognitive processes when faced with adversity and stress. Kilbert and others (2014) reinforce this notion when discussing the negative impacts of perfectionism. Often, self-defeating attitudes related to perfectionism (e.g., I'm a failure; I'm not good enough) can reduce well-being by reinforcing negative self-appraisals. As we've previously mentioned, mental health struggles such as depression and anxiety can often result from irrational beliefs (Warren & Hale, 2020). Adopting a healthy approach to goal setting and avoiding unrealistic expectations or irrational responses to stress are vital to support college students' wellness and quality of life. Perfectionism can be harmful in multiple ways (e.g., mental health, academic success), and college students who focus on increasing resilience through multiple dimensions of wellness can buffer some of those potential negative outcomes. Again, it is important to take advantage of resources within the college environment.

How college students interact with their environments can directly impact their academic wellness and emotional wellness. For example, in a study of over a thousand medical students in Brazil, researchers found those with higher resilience levels reported having a higher quality of life and feeling better about their positions in relation to achieving their goals than those with lower levels of resilience. Similarly, medical students with higher levels of resilience reported lower levels of anxiety and depression compared to their peers with lower levels of resilience. In her dissertation, Davidson (2016) reported her first-generation college student participants suggested that, in addition to family influences, the way they accrued educational opportunities and resources (e.g., mentors, beneficial peers, educational programs and opportunities) was vital to their success in college. Participants also applied internal assets, such as determination and self-efficacy, among others, to persist and achieve success. When college students apply areas of wellness to increase resiliency, academic success is likely to follow.

Spiritual Wellness and Resiliency

As we continue our journey through the seven dimensions of wellness and the implications of their relationship to resiliency for college students, it is important to remember that there is often interplay among different dimensions of wellness. For example, as we discussed in the environment section, the environment often offers college students opportunities related to the other dimensions of wellness that increase resilience. Researchers wonder, though: As college students take advantage of these opportunities, what exactly are they striving toward in their work? One group of authors (Ceary et al., 2019) propose college students may be striving toward valued living. If college students are striving toward valued living, then the actions they take every day will result in a sense of meaning in their lives.

This sense of meaning, whether it be reflective of their values or related specifically to a spiritual or religious path, will increase resilience (Ceary, et al., 2019; Long, 2011).

As college students take daily action to live out their values, it can help reinforce a sense of purpose to their life. These actions reflect spiritual wellness. The benefits of living a life that reflects a sense of meaning is clear. Ceary and colleagues (2019) found not only that valued living was connected to resilience but that it also buffered some of the effects of stressful life events. So, even as life gets stressful in college, those who strive daily to live their value systems will be able to handle that stress more effectively. Further, it may be that, as far as building resilience, how people pursue their values through daily living may be more impactful than a highly active religious life. For example, Ganguly and Perera (2019) found that for college students with disabilities, it was a combination of factors that increased resilience. Students who were adaptable, perceived their relationships as secure, exerted some personal control over their environments, invested effort in persevering toward their goals, and managed stress while perceiving benefits from encountering difficulties increased their resilience. These students tended to have average levels of spirituality resources. Conversely, in her dissertation, Long (2011) found daily spiritual experiences, among other factors, increased resilience. One of the other factors was a higher level of values, which aligns with the research conducted by Ceary and colleagues (2019). Thus, it may be that daily acts that reflect their value systems and a daily spiritual practice will increase resilience for college students.

Physical Wellness and Resiliency

The final dimension of wellness that will be briefly reviewed here and expounded upon in further depth later in the book is physical wellness. College students are often fortunate to have various resources on campus that can, if used wisely, benefit their physical wellness. For example, food plans can provide college students balanced meals, complete with vegetables, other greens, and other healthy foods. However, to achieve wellness, we must choose to pursue healthy options and not consistently eat pizza and burgers for every meal. The environmental resources are often available to us at college; it is up to us to make a daily practice of taking advantage of them. Recreation centers are another resource often available on college campuses. Recreation centers often offer workout equipment, gymnasiums, classes, and coaching. These resources are paid for by student fees. Students should take advantage of what their tuition and fees are paying for.

The positive use of exercise and diet to achieve and maintain a healthy body and mind is not only conducive to increases in wellness; it also increases resilience (Barger et al., 2017; Skrove et al., 2013). The benefits of physical activity are extensive. In the context of wellness and resilience, however, it is clear that physical activity directly relates to higher levels of resilience (Barger et al., 2017). Healthy lifestyles that include physical activity are also related to decreases in anxiety and depression in adolescents (Skrove et al., 2013). In addition to its positive impacts on mental health, exercise has profound positive impacts on cardiovascular health, as people who engage in moderate exercise frequently show lower resting heart rates and reduced risk of cardiovascular disease (Nystoriak & Bhatnagar, 2018). Physical wellness is a key component that can positively impact other domains of wellness, as when we exercise, it has a ripple effect across other domains of wellness. It helps clear our minds and uplift our emotions, and it has the potential to increase positive social connectedness if we exercise with others and take advantage of environmental opportunities through using jogging paths, taking exercise classes at the recreation center, or using elliptical machines (for example). Physical activity is a key component of wellness and one we would be wise to incorporate into routine practice.

Summary

Wellness is a healthcare philosophy that encompasses an active preventative and self-caring lifestyle. A model of a wellness lifestyle is comprised of domains such as cognitive, physical, and emotional self-regulation. Each of these domains can be used to think about how to be more resilient in our choices and behaviors in the face of stresses and strains.

References

American College Health Association. (2014). *American College Health Association—National college health assessment II: Reference group executive summary spring 2014*. Author.

Barger, J., Vitale, P., Gaughan, J. P., & Feldman-Winter, L. (2017). Measuring resilience in the adolescent population: A succinct tool for outpatient adolescent health. *The Journal of Pediatrics, 189*, 201–206. http://dx.doi.org10.1016/j.jpeds.2017.06.030

Beasley, M., Thompson, T., & Davidson, J. (2003). Resilience in response to life stress: The effects of coping style and cognitive hardiness. *Personality and Individual Differences, 34*, 77–95. https://doi.org/10.1016/S0191-8869(02)00027-2

Beiter, R., Nash, R., McCrady, M., Rhoades, D., Linscomb, M., Clarahan, M., & Sammut, S. (2015). The prevalence and correlates of depression, anxiety, and stress in a sample of college students. *Journal of Affective Disorders, 173*, 90–96.

Bluth, K., Mullarkey, M., & Lathren, C. (2018). Self-compassion: A potential path to adolescent resilience and positive exploration. *Journal of Child and Family Studies, 27*, 3037–3047. https://doi.org/10.1007/s10826-018-1125-1

Ceary, C. D., Donahue, J. J., & Shaffer, K. (2019). The strength of pursuing your values: Valued living as a path to resilience among college students. *Stress and Health, 35*, 532–541. https://www.doi.org/10.1002/smi.2886

Center for Collegiate Mental Health. (2020, January). *2019 annual report* (Publication No. STA 20-244). https://ccmh.memberclicks.net/assets/docs/2019-CCMH-Annual-Report_3.17.20.pdf

Chung, H., Klein, M. C., Silverman, D., Corson-Rikert, J., Davidson, E., Ellis, P., & Kasnakian, C. (2011). A pilot for improving depression care on college campuses: Results of the College Breakthrough Series-Depression (CBS-D) project. *Journal of American College Health, 59*(7), 628–639.

Davison, J. V. T. (2016). *Paths of academic resilience: The educational stories of first-generation, low-income students and the processes that led to their experiences of success in the first year of college* [Unpublished doctoral dissertation]. North Carolina State University.

Francis, P. C., & Horn, A. S. (2017). Mental health issues and counseling services in U.S. higher education: An overview of recent research and recommended practices. *Higher Education Policy, 30*(2), 263–277.

Ganguly, R., & Perera, H. N. (2019). Profiles of psychological resilience in college students with disabilities. *Journal of Psychoeducational Assessment, 37*(5), 635–651. http://doi.org/10.1177/0734282918783604

Griffin, C. B., Gray, D. L., Hope, E. C., Metzger, I. W., & Henderson, D. X. (2020). Do coping responses and racial identity promote school adjustment among Black youth? Applying an equity-elaborated social-emotional learning lens. *Urban Education*, 1–26. http://doi.org/10.1177/0042085920933346

Klibert, J., Lamis, D. A., Collins, W., Smalley, K. B., Warren, J. C., Yancey, C. T., & Winterowd, C. (2014). Resilience mediates the relations between perfectionism and college student distress. *Journal of Counseling & Development, 92*, 75–82.

Long, S. L. (2011). *The relationship between religiousness/spirituality and resilience in college students* [Unpublished dissertation]. Texas Woman's University.

National Institute of Mental Health (2017, November). *Prevalence of any anxiety disorder*. https://www.nimh.nih.gov/health/statistics/any-anxiety-disorder.shtml

National Institute of Mental Health (2019, February). *Prevalence of major depressive disorder among adults*. https://www.nimh.nih.gov/health/statistics/major-depression.shtml

Neff, K. D. (2003). The development and validation of a scale to measure self-compassion. *Self and Identity, 2*, 223–250.

Neff, K. D., Hsieh, Y., & Dejitterat, K. (2005). Self-compassion, achievement goals, and coping with academic failure. *Self and Identity, 4*, 263–287. http://doi.org/10.1080/13576500444000317

Neff, K. D., Rude, S. S., & Kirkpatrick, K. L. (2007). An examination of self-compassion in relation to positive psychological functioning and personality traits. *Journal of Research in Personality, 41*, 908–916. http://doi.org/10.1016/j.jrp.2006.08.002

Neenan, M. (2018). *Developing resilience: A cognitive-behavioural approach* (2nd ed.). Routledge.

Nilsson, J. E., Berkel, L. A., Flores, L. Y., & Lucas, M. S. (2004). Utilization rate and presenting concerns of international students at a university counseling center: Implications for outreach programming. *Journal of College Student Psychotherapy, 19*(2), 49–59.

Nystoriak, M. A., & Bhatnagar, A. (2018). Cardiovascular effects and benefits of exercise. *Frontiers in Cardiovascular Medicine, 5*(135), 1–11. https://doi.org/10.3389/fcvm.2018.00135

Rogers, H. B. (2013). Mindfulness meditation for increasing resilience in college students. *Psychiatric Annals, 43*(12), 545–548.

Schiele, M. A., & Domschke, K. (2018). Epigenetics at the crossroads between genes, environment and resilience in anxiety disorders. *Genes, Brain and Behavior, 17*, 1–15. https://doi.org/ doi: 10.1111/gbb.12423

Skrove, M., Romundstad, P., & Indredavik, M. S. (2013). Resilience, lifestyle and symptoms of anxiety and depression in adolescence: The Young-HUNT study. *Social Psychiatry and Psychiatric Epidemiology, 48*(3), 407–416. https://doi.org/10.1007/s00127-012-0561-2

Smyth, J. M., Hockemeyer, J. R., Heron, K. E., Wonderlich, S. A., & Pennebaker, J. W. (2008). Prevalence, type, disclosure, and severity of adverse life events in college students. *Journal of American College Student Health, 57*, 69–76. https://doi.org/10.3200/JACH.57.1.69-76

Tempski, P., Santos, I. S., Mayer, F. B., Enns, S. C., Perotta, B., Paro, H. B., Gannam, S., Peleias, M., Garcia, V. L., Baldassin, S., Guimaraes, K. B., Silva, N. R., da Cruz, E. M., Tofoli, L. F., Silveira, P. S., & Martins, M. A. (2015). Relationship among medical student resilience, educational environment and quality of life. *PloS One, 10*(6). https://doi.org/10.1371/journal.pone.0131535

Ungar, M. (2013). Resilience, trauma, context, and culture. *Trauma, Violence, & Abuse, 14*(3), 255–266. https:// 10.1177/1524838013487805

van Breda, A. D. (2018). A critical review of resilience theory and its relevance for social work. *Social Work, 54*(1), 1–18. https://dx.doi.org/10.15270/54-1-611

Warren, J. M., & Hale, R. W. (2020). Predicting grit and resilience: Exploring college students' academic rational beliefs. *Journal of College Counseling, 23*, 154–167. http://doi.org/10.1002/jocc.12156

Zimmerman, M. A., Stoddard, S. A., Eisman, A. B., Caldwell, C. H., Aiyer, S. M., & Miller, A. (2013). Adolescent resilience: Promoting factors that inform prevention. *Child Development Perspectives, 7*(4), 215–220. http://doi.org/10.1111/cdep.12042

CHAPTER 2

Cognitive Resilience

Paul F. Granello, PhD, LPCC-S, CWC

Thinking: The Core of Resilience

Imagine:

> It is the first day of college, and you are excited to meet your new roommate and see your dorm room. You enter your room and find your roommate is already there. They say, "Did you look out the window? We are right above the dumpsters. I cannot believe it! It's going to stink in here all the time." You go over to the window and look out, and indeed, there are six or seven big dumpsters right outside your window. Your roommate continues, "I hate this room. This is typical, things always happen to me. I hate this college." You are at a choice point: do you join in and continue to complain with your roommate, or do you take a different path? Your choice is important, as it will guide how you will feel about the situation. Will you be concerned, laugh, or be worried, anxious, depressed or some other emotion? It all depends on how you think about it.

Image 2.1

In this chapter, you will learn some ways in which thinking can affect your feelings. You will look at an ABC model for mapping out and changing your thinking. Then you will examine some common thinking errors people make and learn that by substituting coping thoughts, we can change how we feel. It should become apparent that the more you are consciously in control of your thinking, the more resilient you can become as you respond to difficult situations.

Lastly, you will learn about some types of resilient strategies (strengths) for how you can think in a more healthy and well way. For example, the more thinking you do about your thinking, the more you will realize that you are indeed in control of what you choose to think. Developing strengths like tolerating negative emotions, examining emotions as messengers, problem-solving, working through problems, and finding social affirmation can build your self-confidence and lead to happier outcomes for your life and relationships. Ultimately, you will see that we can build resilient strengths though awareness and practice.

Faulty Thinking and Emotional Upset

You've heard it before: "You are what you think you are." But let us unpack and explore this saying. What do we really mean when we say that thinking is at the heart of resilience?

Why? Because what we choose to think drives our emotions. What we choose to think about our perceptions of the world drive powerful emotions that can bring us up or down. It is very important to "think well," to perceive accurately the other people around us. Further, chronic negative emotions can affect our mental and physical health. Rational thinking will make us more resilient and lead us to experience fewer negative emotions and emotional upset.

All the way back to the ancient Greeks, people have argued **that it is not events that upset us but our beliefs about them that matter.** A very useful way to illustrate this philosophy is the ABC model. In this model:

A = Activating event—any event, situation, or encounter

B = Belief—our perception of and belief about the Activating Event

C = Emotional consequence—the emotions that result due to our beliefs

Our thinking is very fast. It is almost automatic in response to events. Most of the time, this is a great survival mechanism. Due to our very automatic thinking, we may come to believe that thinking works by going from A to C or that events cause us to feel a certain way (e.g., trash cans make us angry). This is not correct. Thinking goes from B to C, and the external event can be appraised in a multitude of ways. In other words, we see the trashcans (A) and then decide to be angry based on our belief (B) about them. If we change our belief (B; "Trashcans are not that bad; maybe it will become a running joke"), it is likely that we will have a different emotional consequence (C). Table 2.1 gives another example of how two people can experience the same activating event (A) and yet end up feeling different emotional consequences because their beliefs are quite different. The table also shows how examining our beliefs about a situation and realigning our thinking with more coping kinds of beliefs can lead us to feel differently about a situation.

TABLE 2.1 ABC Model of Cognitive-Emotional Functioning					
Person	Activating Event (A)	Belief (B)	Emotional Consequence (C)	Dispute (D)	New Emotional (E) State
Darcy	RAIN	I love a rainy morning. I will stay inside and watch old movies and eat chocolate.	Happy		
Paul	RAIN	Lousy rain, ruining my day. I can't get outside and work in my garden. This is unfair.	Angry	It is not so bad. I guess I can do something else inside until the rain stops.	Acceptance

Now you can see our thinking and beliefs can influence how we perceive the world around us, which then influences our emotional lives. It would be interesting to look at the types of common thinking errors people make.

Common Thinking Errors

These are the types of errors people make when they assess activating events as negative. Table 2.2 contains examples of common thinking errors or faulty beliefs most people have. The important thing is to be aware of when you are making the error and substitute a better line of thinking in its place. These better types of thinking are called disputes (D), or coping thoughts. Disputes counteract the error in thinking by taking a more reasonable and positive approach.

Demanding

As an example, one particular type of faulty thinking is "demanding." Demanding is thinking that can be identified when we use words like "should," "ought," and "must." While we may think things in life should, ought, or must be a certain way, realistically, they often turn out differently than our demands. When this happens, it is easy to become emotionally upset because our rigid demanding thinking has not been met. A useful substitute for demanding thinking is to use a "preference" thought instead.

Demand: "I must make an A on every exam this semester, and I am a failure if I don't."
Preference: "I would prefer it if I could make an A on every exam. But if not, I will study more and do my best."

Preference thoughts are less demanding and more reasonable. They reflect the fact that there are often factors and variables in the world over which we do not have control—for example, a demanding or critical parent. The world simply does not do as we want all the time, no matter how much we may demand it to do so.

Now that you are familiar with some typical thinking errors, look back at the scene at the start of this chapter. Can you identify what types of thinking errors the roommate was making?

Learning to evaluate your thinking can be a major cognitive strength in life. No longer are you the victim of random events or faulty beliefs, but instead, you are the master of your own thinking. Once you master replacing poor thinking with rational thought, you will also experience fewer and less intense negative emotions.

EXERCISE 2.1: THOUGHT SUBSTITUTION

Knowing what some of your common thinking errors are now empowers you to stop and replace them with more coping kinds of thinking. Fold a sheet of paper lengthwise and make two columns. In column one, put "Errors." In column two, put "Coping Thoughts." List three thinking errors that may apply to you and write three coping thoughts you can substitute in the second column. Pick one of your coping thoughts each time you catch yourself thinking in error and substitute your coping thought instead.

BOX 2.1: SOCIAL MEDIA

It is easy to have thinking errors when on social media. What is presented on social media is a person's "best foot forward." In other words, the picture is what the presenter wants you to see. This can be more or less an accurate representation of reality, depending on the presenter's intentions. You need to be careful in interpreting the virtual as real. In the absence of context, messages can be interpreted in many ways. It is up to you to "buy it" or "just leave it."

Between stimuli and response, there is space. In that space is our power to choose our response. In our response lies our growth and our freedom.

—Victor Frankl

TABLE 2.2 Common Thinking Errors		
Thinking Error	**Example**	**Refute**
Perfectionism	"I must always get everything right the first time."	"Some things take time to learn or change. I can learn from my mistakes, and that is okay."
Catastrophizing	"Even small things are awful, and nothing is going my way."	"I will notice when even a small thing goes my way and is positive."
Minimize the Positive	"My boss gave me a compliment. I wonder what he wants from me now."	"It is nice to get a compliment from my boss."
Maximize the Negative	"I made a mistake on my report. I am so dumb. Why can't I get anything right?"	"I am not dumb because I made a mistake. I will learn from it and not repeat it in the future."
Emotional Reasoning	"I am anxious and I feel bad, so something must be wrong."	"Feelings are just messengers about how I am thinking. I can choose to think differently and feel better."
Mind Reading	"My friend has not called me in a while, so they must be mad at me."	"I will call my friend and find out how they are doing and what they are thinking."
Demanding	"My professor should be more fair to me and should give me extra time on my exam."	"I would prefer it if the professor gave us more time, but if not, I can cope and still do well."
Faulty Comparison	"Everyone else is perfectly fine. What is wrong with me?	"No one is perfectly fine. Everyone has their stuff. I am just being human."
Unrealistic Expectation	"If my girlfriend really loves me. she will text me throughout the day today."	"I know she is also busy with her stuff."

Resilient Strengths

Just as one can build their physical strength or skill set by working out and practicing, you can build your cognitive resilience through developing strategies/strengths and practicing. You are now ready to examine some resiliency strategies. The rest of this chapter is a list of some strategies you may wish to consider when building your resilience.

Interaction of Thoughts and Emotions

Tolerating Negative Emotions

For just about everyone, life does not always go the way we want it to go. Life will hand you adversity. You are human and will have emotions. Sometimes emotions are uplifting, hopeful, and happy. Other times, they are negative and bring you down. Consider letting yourself learn to let yourself feel the good and bad emotions. Even though they may feel powerful, emotions are just the result of our thinking patterns about particular events. You can learn to tolerate—not like, but put up with—negative emotions until you can sort them out or change them by changing your thinking. When emotions are negative, such as anger or anxiety, you do not have to immediately distract yourself from them. You can instead look to evaluate them and think about what meaning they may have for you.

Emotions as Messengers

One strategy for coping with negative emotions is to understand them as messengers about our thinking. Some people report they are more in touch with their emotions than their thoughts. This is fine. Emotions can serve as messengers about beliefs. Behind each emotion is a theme of belief or underlying belief. Table 2.3 below shows some of the common underlying beliefs for some common emotions. Once you know the underlying theme, you can examine your thinking and substitute thoughts that are more rational. Chances are the emotional intensity of what you are feeling will be reduced. Changing your thinking may not remove negative emotions entirely. Sometimes being resilient means learning to tolerate negative emotions. We don't have to like something in order to cope with it positively.

TABLE 2.3 Emotional Messages	
Emotion	**Message and Underlying Belief**
Anger	"It's unfair"; "This is unjust." You believe you or someone you care about has been treated unfairly.
Sadness	"This is a loss"; "I have lost and cannot repair the damage." You believe you have experienced a loss and it is not fixable.
Jealousy	"I want it." You believe you deserve what someone else has received.
Guilt	"I should not have done that." You have violated one of your core values.
Happiness	"I feel good." Your thinking and behavior are coherent, and you believe you are achieving your goals.

BOX 2.2: CULTURAL COMPETENCY

People from different cultures can see the world from different viewpoints than you do. They may hold different beliefs about people, places, and things and therefore have different emotions in response to events. It is an error to think everyone thinks the same as you do. It is important to "check in" with people who come from different cultures to make sure you and they are interpreting events with some common ideas.

The Best Way Out Is Always Through

Negative emotions are not fun to feel. Anger, sadness, anxiety, and loneliness can lead us to resentment and avoidance. However, avoiding a situation, person, or thing in the short term may make you temporarily feel okay, but it will not lead to less stress in the end. The saying "The best way out is always through" means that facing up to one's predicaments and deadlines is always better than procrastinating. People, because they do not like to feel negative emotions, can develop self-defeating thoughts and behaviors and even addictions to exercise, alcohol, food, drugs, shopping, video games, or other distractions, whereas tolerating negative emotions and working through a difficult challenge will make you feel empowered and satisfied with yourself for a job well done.

Social Affirmation and Support

Sometimes when we are sad or hurt, we withdraw from people. We believe we cannot be hurt further if we distance ourselves from others. In the short term, this may be acceptable because we need to gather ourselves so we can begin to evaluate and examine the situation. However, withdrawal or isolation as a chronic or long-term strategy does not work. We need others to give us support, particularly in difficult times. From a thinking perspective, we need others to help us work through identifying and modifying our beliefs. We need others to "bounce" our thinking off of. Getting affirmation from others about our good thinking and having them challenge our errors in thinking can be helpful. Find someone you trust—not just anyone—and share why you are upset. Perhaps they can help you sort it out.

Problem Solving

As a child, you learned to problem-solve by trial and error or by watching others cope with problems. Sometimes you learned the hard way by experiencing failure and frustration first before finding strategies that helped you achieve your goal. Sometimes you had good role models you could emulate, and other times, you had bad models who, if emulated, led to your own frustration. As an adult, you can learn problem-solving strategies that can help you avoid the pitfalls of trial-and-error or observation approaches. One such model is the IDEAL (Identify, Define, Explore, Act, Learn) problem-solving model. IDEAL is an acronym that stands for:

EXERCISE 2.2: REFRAMING

Reframing helps you look at a situation in a new light and results in a different attitude toward it. Start by considering a situation that is causing you concern or is upsetting to you. Think about the situation as objectively as you can. Then write down the facts of the situation. Try not to be to hung up on the emotional consequences. Instead, focus on just the facts. Now step back and look at your list of facts. Can you create another alternate explanation for the list of facts that's different and more acceptable to you than your current interpretation? Entertain this new explanation for a while. Realize the facts have not changed: just your view of them has (modified beliefs). You may even get a sense of relief about the situation now that you see it in a different light.

Identify
See a situation as a problem that needs to be fixed. It is important to decide if a situation or event needs your attention or is even a problem. Sometimes a "molehill" is not worth getting upset over or investing your energy into solving. If an event needs to be solved, then you need to define it.

Define
Accurately defining the problem can help you find a workable solution—maybe not the ideal or perfect solution, but one that will work and get you on your way. Try to define the problem by making a few statements. For example: My boyfriend is overprotective. I want him to stop monitoring my interactions with other people. This is a short and direct definition.

Explore
Once you have a good definition of the problem to be solved, it is time to brainstorm solutions. The idea is to come up with several possible courses of action and then choose the best possible course. It is important to let yourself come up with some creative solutions and not just choose the first solution you generate.

Act
Okay, now you have your course of action chosen, and it is time to act. Procrastinating or not acting at all will not get a problem solved. Get support from others if you are reluctant or intimidated about taking action.

Learn
Evaluate your action and the results you got from following a certain course of action. If things did not turn out perfectly, it is okay. The point is that you can learn from a mistake, modify your thinking and behavior, and try again.

Applying a model like IDEAL can also help you slow down and think through a situation before you just react to it. Just reacting to a situation can sometimes lead to more confusion and emotional upset than necessary. Slow down and think through things before you jump to respond to a situation.

EXERCISE 2.3: APPLY IDEAL

Think of a recent problem situation that you needed to solve. Apply the IDEAL model to the situation. What type of solution did you produce? Can you evaluate it and learn for next time?

Be Curious

Research has shown that being curious about the world in general makes us more cognitively well. Intellectual stimulation and being curious are two factors that can help you stay more resilient. When in a difficult situation, step back from it and look at it from a new vantage point. Ask yourself questions about the situation: *What can I learn here? What is the relationship of this situation to my life? Is it very important in the big picture?* By adopting a curious attitude, you will distance yourself from the difficulties to have a new and perhaps helpful perspective.

EXERCISE 2.4: POSITIVE GRATITUDE

Many people negate the positive. For example, they get a compliment and dismiss it. One way to build up resilience is to focus on the positive and enhance it through daily gratitude exercises. Try this for 30 days. Each evening before you go to sleep, write down three positive things for which you are grateful about the day you just lived. They do not have to be big things—maybe something small, like how a flower looked or that you spoke with a friend. You can even repeat your sources of gratitude across multiple days. The important thing is to become actively aware and appreciative (grateful) for the positive things in your life. You may also want to start your day by identifying three things you are grateful for each morning.

Write three gratitude statements:

BOX 2.3: DUE TO THE PANDEMIC

A lot of change has occurred in a short period due to the pandemic. Rapid change can lead to stress. People are working from home, taking classes online, and having to social distance. Yet most people are coping even if they would prefer other circumstances. How have you been tested during this time? You may have had to change your thinking. Perhaps you can use some of the thinking strategies in this chapter to help you cope.

Summary

Thinking straight means realistically examining our own thinking, recognizing errors, and substituting better coping strategies. In this chapter, we first examined how our thinking can influence our emotional life by learning the ABC model. Next, we looked at how faulty thinking may lead to emotional upset and confusion. All people make errors in thinking from time to time. Recognize your common errors and learn to dispute them with more positive thoughts and ideas.

Finally, we examined some resilient strengths or coping strategies concerned with how we could modify our thinking.

I strongly encourage you to try the exercises and the reflection questions in this chapter, as they provide more ways to improve your thinking and therefore your resilience and cognitive wellness.

Cognitive Wellness and Resiliency Tips

A list of tips for achieving resiliency in the cognitive domain

1. Monitor your thinking: What are your common thinking errors?
2. Problem-solve using the IDEAL model.
3. Emotions are messengers: look for the underlying theme.
4. Use positive self-talk and gratitude statements to bolster your mood.
5. Use reframing to look at a situation from a different perspective.
6. Look for the theme behind an emotion.
7. Pursue cognitive stimulation and meaning in life.
8. Check out your thinking with a close friend.
9. The best way out is always through.
10. Find meaning in daily life; identify themes in your thinking by keeping a daily journal.

Reflection Questions

1. Think about your own thinking (metacognition). Do you always think well? Probably not. What are some of the common thinking errors you fall into regularly?
2. Apply the ABC model to a recent situation in which you were emotionally upset. What was the activating event, your beliefs, and emotional consequence? How could you examine or substitute more rational refuting or coping thoughts?
3. What can you do to improve your quality of thinking? One strategy is to start a daily journal. In your journal, you can write down your thoughts and feelings and reflect upon them. What meaning can you create from your thoughts? What themes emerge over time?

References

Elmore, T., & McPeak, A. (2019). *Generation Z unfiltered: Facing nine hidden challenges of the most anxious population*. Poet Gardener.

Erford, B. J. (2015). *Forty techniques every counselor should know* (2nd edition). Pearson.

Granello, P. F. (2013). *Wellness: Achieving a healthy lifestyle*. Pearson.

Neenan, M. (2018). *Developing Resilience: A cognitive behavioral approach*. Routledge.

Seligman, M. E. (2011). *Flourish: A visionary new understanding of happiness and well-being*. Free Press.

Travis, J. W., & Ryan, R. S. (2004). *Wellness workbook: How to achieve enduring health and vitality*. Celestial Arts.

Credit

CHAPTER 3

Emotional Resilience

Matthew S. Fleming, MA, MS, LPCC-S

The Ultimate Path
is without difficulty;
just avoid picking and choosing.

—Yuanwu et al.

Image 3.1

Introduction

Emotional resilience (ER) refers to the ability to weather difficulties as they arise. Emotional resilience varies from person to person, with some people seeming to be able to weather incredible hardships with grace while other people burst into tears when they encounter seemingly minor difficulties. Entrance into college has always been a time for many adjustments and challenges as students leave their homes, high schools, parents, and established friend groups. Upon arriving on campus, they are faced with challenges, including financial concerns, more difficult subject matter, learning to be responsible for themselves without the benefit of parental oversight, and integrating into new social circles. Such "normal" stresses have been exacerbated in 2020 as students contend with class disruptions due to a pandemic and the need to reduce the spread of the COVID-19 virus. All of these changes can culminate in upset for students who are not emotionally ready to bounce back from the multitude of challenges.

Students who have not developed skills for dealing with the emotional onslaught of all the new things at school may, inadvertently, try to avoid feeling via numbing or distracting. As entry into college provides access to many diversions, some will resort to drinking, drugs, sexual promiscuity, etc. Without judging moderate use of distractions, it is obvious that excessive use of distracting techniques is not sustainable for the student. Often this becomes a crisis for the student, resulting in dropping out, poor performance, or (best case) heading to the student counseling center for support.

All of this begs the question: Can ER be enhanced to enable students to better cope and deal with multiple difficulties? The general consensus is that ER can be enhanced with a variety of methods. Wright and Masten (2005) suggest improvements to resilience can be made through "ordinary" interventions that address deficits in resilience. These interventions are generally identified through assessing deficits and formulating a plan to improve confidence in one's ability to overcome adversity.

ER Background

The literature pertaining to ER is very extensive and beyond comprehensive discussion in this chapter. However, we can look at some key topics and suggest further reading.

Sarrionandia and Mikolajczak (2020) analyzed 522 articles to assess the relationship between emotional intelligence (EI) and physical health. They focused on 106 studies they felt were most relevant in relating emotional intelligence and health. They concluded that EI correlated most closely with social support and sleep. Not surprisingly, they also identified relationships among diet, physical activity, and substance abuse. The importance of social support cannot be underestimated, and their insights suggest training to overcome social deficits might serve to increase EI and physical health. The paper identifies areas where further research is needed to establish other relationships between EI and health.

Emotions are often thought of as very brief, transitory events lasting at most a few minutes. Verduyn et al. (2009) studied fear, anger, joy, gratitude, and sadness episodes to measure the duration of these reactions. They concluded that many of the emotions lasted as long as several days. A large contributor to the duration of an emotion seemed to be the amount of rumination the individual engaged in. Rumination is thought to be passive and usually does not result in improving the situation.

Verduyn et al. (2015) suggest some help may be offered to reduce rumination and return from a difficult emotion more quickly. Reappraisal of the situation may allow the individual to change their conclusions about the event that triggered the emotion. A second reappraisal strategy is to distance oneself from the event as well. Verduyn also discussed distraction as a coping mechanism. This strategy can be effective as long as the distraction itself does not increase distress (e.g., getting drunk and then dealing with the aftermath). The good news is that it is possible to learn to ruminate less and to use reappraisal more.

TABLE 3.1 Rumination and Better Ways to Cope

Skill	What It Looks Like	Accomplishes	Emotion Triggered
Rumination (not usually helpful)	"I can't believe I messed up on that test. I am so stupid."	Feels helpless, stupid cannot be fixed. Self-focused.	Hopeless, worthless, less than okay.
Reappraisal	"I did poorly on that test. Let's see what I can learn from my mistakes and formulate a strategy for my next test."	Hopeful. Looking over past errors facilitates learning.	Hopeful, optimistic. I can do better next time.
Distancing	"I did poorly on that test. I feel bad, but I might feel better if I go for a run."	Gives a break from the situation. Situation can be revisited when the initial reaction cools down.	Take a break from the problem. Use healthy coping that makes you feel more able to pick up the problem later.
Distracting	"I did poorly on that test. I'm going to veg out tonight in front of the TV."	Gives a break but may not contribute to later performance. May help but may also result in procrastination.	Vague sense of unease knowing the problem is still there. Break may be helpful.

Your History Matters

The ability to muster emotional resilience is also dependent on where and how one is raised (Flouri et al., 2015). Flouri et al. discuss the impact of growing up in poverty and often associated adverse childhood events. Difficult situations/poverty often do not impact the children (except for hunger, etc.), as children are very resilient and adaptable. Flouri suggests the stress of poverty impacts the parents' mental and physical health and may contribute to their depression, anxiety, anger, and substance abuse. This causes the parents to sometimes be unavailable to the children as well as vulnerable to acting out their anger toward the children. Not surprisingly, parents who were still able to be warm and supportive to their children fostered the children's ER, and parental care moderated the impact of the difficult circumstances on the children. This suggests social programs directed at caring for children may also need to address parental stress.

Parenting styles are very important to development of EI. Wang et al. (2019) discuss four main parenting styles and the impact on 3–6-year-old children. These styles are authoritarian (direction without much warmth or support), authoritative (firm rules with warmth and support), democratic (rules that are discussed with the child, who is treated as more of an equal party), and doting (love/support but few rules and the child can do what they please). The best outcomes were with the democratic and authoritative styles, where there were rules either mandated or discussed but the children always knew they were valued and loved. Democratic or authoritative styles were shown to contribute to a child's ability to effectively communicate with peers. Social support is largely borne out of being able to communicate with one's peers, and this is perceived as protective to EI.

Alegre and Benson (2010) further emphasize that parental availability is most predictive of adolescent anxiety and depression. Parents who are not available invalidate the adolescent's emotions and feelings, leaving the adolescent confused about their own appraisal of the world and its impact on them. Alegre and Benson also suggest that disciplining and even harsh punishment seem to have minimal impact in terms of promoting future internalizing (depression/anxiety) episodes.

Ruella Frank discusses how infants come to know themselves (2001; Frank & La Barre, 2011). Frank has contributed to work on movement-based psychotherapy she refers to as developmental somatic psychotherapy, which uses a felt sense of a person's movements (both by the client and the therapist) as a means to explore emotional difficulties. Frank suggests infants do not have a sense of themselves at birth. According to Frank, when a newborn makes a motion or utters a sound, the infant looks to the expression/reaction of the parent. If the parent is congruent in their response, the infant gradually internalizes the parental expressions as their own. Mismatches in the parent/child interactions can result in frustration for the child in an impaired ability to negotiate appropriate responses to stimuli. For example, if a parent is depressed and takes the infant's attempts to get away to explore as a personal rejection, the parent may clutch their child more tightly. The child may react either by escalating their attempts to leave (aggression) or may give up (depression). While it might be intimidating to new parents to think they must match the energy of their children moment to moment (exhausting), Frank suggests a more hopeful conclusion: that a parent who is appropriately responsive 30% of the time will likely meet the child's needs.

Image 3.2

A study on adverse childhood events (ACE) surveyed over 13,000 people from a large HMO regarding their exposure to difficult events/situations while growing up (Felitti et al., 1998). "Seven categories of adverse childhood experiences were studied: psychological, physical, or sexual abuse; violence against mother; or living with household members who were substance abusers, mentally ill or suicidal, or ever imprisoned" (p.1). The study showed a correlation between ACE events and problems in adulthood, including a 4- to 12-fold increase in health risks for alcoholism, drug abuse, depression, and suicide attempts. The study also noted relationships between adverse events and poor adult health outcomes. This correlation might be due to the poor EI/ER that resulted from difficult environments and the use of substances, alcohol, eating, and other means to avoid the internalized messages from said abusive environment. The Centers for Disease Control and Prevention (CDC) indicates nearly one in four people have histories with three or more significant adverse situations occurring to them (CDC, 2020).

Many people think that you should "just get over" past abuse or lesser emotional hurts. This may sound like a good idea, but childhood (and even later) experiences change the nervous system in ways that take effort to repair. Bessel van der Kolk (2014) writes extensively about how trauma (remember some traumas are "small" but important) may reside in the body until dealt with. Van der Kolk's work is extensively used as a reference in trauma therapy.

Steven Porges (2012a) writes about how trauma interferes with our ability to socially connect. Porges suggests that for a connection with another person to occur, the conditions of safety, proximity, contact, and bonds must be present. For individuals who have early trauma, Porges states that the vagus nerve actually remodels itself in ways that impact the ability to process cues from the other (a smile, frown, etc.) and, moreover, may reduce the person's ability to respond appropriately. This impairs the person's ability to connect to others and this further exacerbates negative self-talk. The vagus nerve impacts one's ability to generate facial cues that help with bonding to another person or even to show distress. Normal reactions to distress include flight or fight. In those with impaired vagus nerve tone, they might react to stress with a racing heartbeat but show no outward signs of their experience. Porges suggests several "hacks" to improve vagus nerve tone that are covered later in this chapter.

How to Build Emotional Resilience

It is important to differentiate between thinking and emotions. At a high level, thoughts/feelings can be differentiated by the test of saying "I think (idea or thought)." For example, "I think sad" makes less sense than "I feel sad," which is a statement of how the person is experiencing the world at the moment. If you can substitute the word "think" for "feel" in a statement and the statement still makes sense, you are more likely referring to a thought than a feeling.

Emotions are the bodily felt sense of our reactions to the world. As noted in Verduyn (2015), thoughts (rumination) can cause emotions to last for hours or days. Cognitive therapies seek to adjust thinking patterns to help a person replace rumination with more helpful ways of framing (thinking about) the situation. Often one will seek to evaluate a cognition as "good or bad" and then replace the "bad" thoughts with more hopeful thoughts. This can be very helpful, as noted in Table 3.1.

Doubt as a Good Thing

It is often helpful to cultivate some doubt about the veracity of a thought we may hold. If we treat our thoughts as "facts," then we risk being tortured by negative self-talk. Byron Katie (2002) suggests four questions that might help challenge thinking by injecting some doubt and, thereby, allow us some space for a better conclusion. She suggests the following questions:

- Do I know this thought is true?
- Can I be entirely sure this thought is true (how can we really know anything absolutely)?
- How do I react when I think that thought?
- Who would I be without that thought (or how would I be)?

This book can be very helpful in self-work for learning how to challenge thought patterns.

Doubt also injects a bit of time between when we are presented with something and when we react. For example, if we believe we know the motivations of another person and they step on our toe, we might think *Wow, that person is really mean, and I am going to punch them.* However, with doubt, we may start to explore other options, like *Maybe they were distracted worrying about a loved one* or *Maybe I had my foot too far out into the aisle*. It is especially important that we doubt whether or not we really know the motivations, as thinking we know is a projection (taking our own interpretation of a situation and assuming the other thinks the same way). When we use doubt in this way, we are given the opportunity to choose how we will respond to the situation in light of what will be most helpful. In the case of having your toe stepped on, helpful responses might be "ouch" or "Can you call the ER, because my toe is broken."

EXERCISE 3.1: HOW WE TELL STORIES

Imagine you are walking down a narrow two-lane street with sidewalks on both sides. On the other side of the street is someone you know walking towards you. You call out their name and wave, but the person does not acknowledge you in any way.

Notice how you feel and what you think

Some people wonder if the person is mad at them or if they "did something wrong" or if the person is hurt or upset.

Now ask *What do I really know?*

Now ask yourself *How shall I respond?*

For example, if you really want to talk, you might jog down to the crosswalk, walk over to your friend, and say "hi." Or you might decide to just let the person pass without doing anything, as it was not important to you.

It is important to think about how you might react to the memory of the incident the next time you see the person. If you carry around the thought *They hate me* because of no response, imagine the quality of your next encounter with that person (not good).

Cognitive therapies can be helpful in challenging thought patterns as long as the challenge is not expected to come up with a black-and-white conclusion. Sometimes the thoughts lead to a personalization of the ideas that may block helpful actions. For example, asking *Am I attractive enough to talk to that guy/girl who I find myself drawn to?* invites a projection of *No one that hot could like me* and then a decision not to talk to the person. It is important to realize that the other person's reaction to you is born out of their own likes/dislikes/upbringing and that you do not know how they will react to you initiating contact. Doubt may not lessen the butterflies that occur as you are starting the conversations, but doubt may give you the chance to begin. You may be surprised at how many times you find a welcoming response from the other person.

How Do We Decide Anything?

Often a new college student is presented with so many options for "how to be" and "how to think" that it may be overwhelming. As college students progress, they often are drawn to ideas they find attractive, and that helps them decide who they will become. Sometimes, however, it is very difficult to decide between disparate life paths. In selecting a career, for example, how does one decide among being a doctor, a plumber, a priest, or an engineer? This decision is important, as it informs the individual in making decisions of what to pursue and what to ignore. For example, deciding to be a priest might cause someone to not pursue engineering mathematics in their studies, as the time might be better spent studying theology.

Ruth Chang (2014) gave a TED Talk on making hard choices. In that talk, Chang discusses how one makes the big or momentous decisions in one's life. Career is one big decision, as are decisions about who to associate with. Chang suggests that when choosing between different options that have good and bad (but different) trade-offs, the primary consideration is the actual choosing and then investing one's energy in pursuing the chosen option. For example, if you want to be a concert pianist, feasibility or your potential may not be obvious today. However, if you are willing to dedicate the time and effort to study and practice, your skills will improve, and someday you may be a professional. It is important to keep in mind that choosing a particular path does not mean it will always be fun or rewarding (e.g., you may have to forgo social events to practice your music). However, the more you work and persist, the better your chances of eventually coming to love the piano. This approach is fundamental for life's other big decisions. For example, the decision to get married will not work out well if you lose sight that marriage is a decision to always act in a way that supports your stated desire to be partnered.

Knowing our authentic selves is of paramount importance in choosing our life directions. When we are in touch with our values, we are better equipped to respond effectively as opportunities are presented to us. Being grounded in knowing when to say "yes" or "no" can save us a lot of unproductive time. This is challenging to do. For example, it sounds great and is easy to say, "I want to be the CEO of a tech startup." However, choosing the CEO route will entail many long hours, hard work, and sacrifices. It might mean you defer marriage, going out to the theater, or walking in the woods. The long hours and hard work are neither good nor bad, but they may or may not be a fit for your values.

On the following two pages is a template for conducting your own value sort and evaluation. Choose a time when you can have between 30–60 minutes to sit quietly with the value sort and values clarification pages. After you identify your most important values, take a few minutes to reflect on whether those values feel "true" to you and why or why not.

EXERCISE 3.2: RATE MY VALUES

Reflection: my top 5 values are:

1.
2.
3.
4.
5.

When I see those values on paper, I am (or am not) able to clarify my directions for:
career
hobbies
partner relationships
my need for free time

Value Sort

1. Read List
   - Feel free to add values not on list
2. Rate the Relative Importance (H – M – L) (Use following chart)
   - Select Highly Important
   - Select Lowest in Importance
   - Rate Remainder M
3. Rank Order the "Highly" Important
   - Select Most Important & Rank #1
   - Select Least Important & Rank #
4. Select the Five Most Important Values

ACHIEVEMENT (sense of accomplishment, mastery)		
ADVANCEMENT (promotion)		
ADVENTURE (new and challenging experiences)		
AFFECTION (love, caring)		
COMPETITIVENESS (winning, taking risks)		
COOPERATION (working well with others, teamwork)		
CREATIVITY (being imaginative, innovative)		
ECONOMIC SECURITY (steady, adequate income)		
FAME (being famous, well known)		
FAMILY HAPPINESS		
FREEDOM (independence, autonomy)		
FRIENDSHIP (close relationships with others)		
HEALTH (being physically and mentally well)		
HELPFULNESS (assisting others, improving society)		
INNER HARMONY (being at peace with yourself)		
INTEGRITY (honesty, sincerity, standing up for beliefs)		
INVOLVEMENT (participating with others, belonging)		
LOYALTY (duty, respectfulness, obedience)		
ORDER (tranquility, stability, conformity)		
PERSONAL DEVELOPMENT (use of potential)		
PLEASURE (fun, laughs, leisurely life-style)		
POWER (control, authority, influence over others)		
RECOGNITION (respect from others, status)		
RELIGION (strong religious beliefs, closeness to God)		
RESPONSIBILITY (accountable for results)		
SELF-RESPECT (pride, sense of personal identity)		
WEALTH (making money, getting rich)		
WISDOM (understanding life, discovering knowledge)		

Values Clarification

Use the the chart below to complete A through D

A. How would you feel if you had a great deal less:
    1. Wouldn't care
    3. Moderately concerned
    5. Devastated

B. How would you feel if you had a great deal more:
    1. Wouldn't matter
    3. Happy
    5. Ecstatic

C. Total A + B and select your five most values

To break a tie:

D. How well have I satisfied this value up to now in my life:
    10. Fully satisfied
    5. Moderately satisfied
    1. Not satisfied at all

A Means to an End
Why do I want _____?
What will it achieve for me?

	A	B	C	D
ACHIEVEMENT (sense of accomplishment, mastery)				
ADVANCEMENT (promotion)				
ADVENTURE (new and challenging experiences)				
AFFECTION (love, caring)				
COMPETITIVENESS (winning, taking risks)				
COOPERATION (working well with others, teamwork)				
CREATIVITY (being imaginative, innovative)				
ECONOMIC SECURITY (steady, adequate income)				
FAME (being famous, well known)				
FAMILY HAPPINESS				
FREEDOM (independence, autonomy)				
FRIENDSHIP (close relationships with others)				
HEALTH (being physically and mentally well)				
HELPFULNESS (assisting others, improving society)				
INNER HARMONY (being at peace with yourself)				
INTEGRITY (honesty, sincerity, standing up for beliefs)				
INVOLVEMENT (participating with others, belonging)				
LOYALTY (duty, respectfulness, obedience)				
ORDER (tranquility, stability, conformity)				
PERSONAL DEVELOPMENT (use of potential)				
PLEASURE (fun, laughs, leisurely life-style)				
POWER (control, authority, influence over others)				
RECOGNITION (respect from others, status)				
RELIGION (strong religious beliefs, closeness to God)				
RESPONSIBILITY (accountable for results)				
SELF-RESPECT (pride, sense of personal identity)				
WEALTH (making money, getting rich)				
WISDOM (understanding life, discovering knowledge)				

Knowing your authentic self is a critical step toward being more satisfied with your life and may even result in a longer life. Victor Frankl, in *Yes to Life* (2019) discussed his ability to survive a Nazi concentration camp during WWII. Frankl discusses the need for a coherent, actionable goal that one can pursue day by day. Frankl talks about how he was planning his lectures to give as a professor in Vienna after the war ended. Frankl said he sewed notes into his garments to retrieve after he was released. Frankl pointed out, however, that the goal selected must not depend on "realizing the goal on a particular day." There were many in the concentration camp who would attach to the idea of a release "in two weeks" based on reports from the front, only to die after their hopes were dashed (perhaps multiple times) as the war dragged on. It is not so different from this chapter's earlier example of wanting to be a pianist. If you decide that you will be "discovered and successful" by a certain date, frustration may arise when that date passes. How many musicians can you think of who had to toil a very long time before their "overnight success"?

Body Awareness

Emotions create feelings in the body that are sometimes pleasant and sometimes unpleasant. When you pet a puppy and it licks your face, you might feel warmth or tingling within your body if you are open to the affection the puppy displays. However, some people may be very afraid of germs from the puppy and may react by pushing the puppy away out of fear of the germs. This "pushing away" knee-jerk reaction is triggered by many of our feelings that we try not to feel. The pushing away can take the form of numbing or distracting oneself from the emotion. Sometimes this is healthy, as in times of crisis so we can deal with the crisis. Often, however, avoiding our emotions means we miss important cues about life or push away nurturing relationships because the intense emotions feel dangerous.

As we push away emotions, we can misinterpret what they are here to tell us. Often we describe an emotional longing as a "hunger," and we might try to eat (or drink) to fill the hole the longing leaves. Eating or drinking is the correct solution if you are really hungry or thirsty. However, we often eat when we feel these feelings:

TABLE 3.2 Longing and Options for Dealing with the Longing		
Longing	**Unhelpful**	**More Helpful/Appropriate**
Hunger/Thirst	Avoid, exercise, etc.	Eat when you are hungry.
Sleepy	Might have caffeine to avoid	Take a power nap.
Boredom	Often eat when bored	What would be enjoyable and fulfilling? Read a book, take a walk.
Stress	Eat, drink alcohol, distract	Evaluate the cause of the stress and determine best approaches for dealing with it.
Effect	Eat to feel "up", drink alcohol to calm down ...	Realize that using food or substances to achieve a particular emotional effect is a road to addiction.
Loneliness	Often eat or drink to distract	If you can realize you are lonely, you can select the better coping option of calling a friend, going to church, or organizing a game night.
Filling a void	Eating, drinking, gambling, etc. to avoid feeling	Address the void. What will really help? Sometimes we just have to stay with the dark night of the soul.

Employing mindfulness while eating can enhance the enjoyment of eating and also help you know why you are eating. A mindful approach involves slowing down because we are drawn to doing everything fast rather than doing it in a way that satisfies. The next time you eat, start by looking at your food with your eyes. Notice what you think/ feel. Notice how your body reacts with excitement (ice cream) or something else (liver and onions). Smell your food and notice your body and thoughts again. How does your stomach feel before and after taking that first bite? Now as you eat, what does your mind think about what you are eating? Notice your heart and whether you are trying to fill a hole in your heart. If memories come up while eating, pause and notice them.

EXERCISE 3.3: MINDFULNESS

Go to YouTube and search for "eating one raisin." Many videos will come up in the search results. Pick a video that leads you through eating one raisin very slowly (choose a video that is 5–10 minutes long, not the hour-long version). This exercise will allow you to notice your reactions both to the raisin and to your slowing down to eat the raisin. Some people will think *I've never really tasted a raisin before* as they experience the raisin in slow motion. Others will think *I got really frustrated going so slow.* The frustration response is just as valid as the pleasure of eating the raisin. It is useful to notice if you experience frustration because you might find that it drives you to eat too fast (power through lunch without actually enjoying it) or to be oblivious and miss fun things because you are in a hurry to get to the next thing.

Often we experience unwelcome emotions like fear/dread or anxiety/worry. Anxiety is often difficult to control, as it comes from the sympathetic nervous system, which is outside our conscious control. The breath provides a back door into the sympathetic nervous system, in that slowing down your breathing also slows your heart rate and has a calming effect. This can result in feeling more relaxed in relatively short order. In learning and practicing deep belly

---

EXERCISE 3.4: BELLY BREATHING

Get comfortable and allow your breathing to be natural. Place one hand on your sternum and one hand on your belly. Notice which hand moves more. When stressed, people tend to breathe more shallowly and into their upper chests (imagine a dog panting), so you may notice your upper hand, which is placed on your sternum, moving more if you are stressed.

- Now we will start with three slow, deep breaths into your belly.
- Imagine you are trying to pop out your belly button, as this helps make contact with the belly.
- Breath in from the nose. Try to breath into your belly completely (not forcefully) in about 5 seconds (you can adjust this as needed).
- Pause the breath for 3 seconds (you can adjust this).
- Breath out slowly through your mouth for about 10 seconds (you can adjust this).
- Repeat two more times.
- Belly breathing should be practiced about three times/day as we are building a relaxation reflex. Start with only three breaths, as there is a tendency to hyperventilate when a person is not used to breathing deeply. Gradually, over a period of 4–6 weeks, work up to doing this exercise for 3–4 minutes three times per day. Now you are ready to employ this for test taking. Just start the test with three breaths. Your body will probably relax, and you can proceed with the exam.

breathing at The Ohio State University, one student commented that belly breathing was "worth 10 extra points on my exam because I can calm down more quickly and get down to the business of the exam." Belly breathing also shows up in some of Porges's writing as a way to engage the vagus nerve "brake" to slow down the heart rate (Porges, 2017). Porges shows that the heart rate tends to speed up with inhalation and slows down during exhalation. This suggests a slight tweak to belly breathing to speed up (slightly) the in breath and slow down the out breath.

Meditation

Meditation supports emotional regulation by teaching us how to stay present with difficulties rather than running away. Too often we simply try to push the difficult or unpleasant emotion away rather than staying with it long enough

to really know what the emotion is and then how to best deal with it. Often just having the emotion is enough for it to dissipate, but not always. Meditation is not a universal remedy or wonder drug. It has limitations as to when and how it can be used effectively.

Meditation teaches us to not attach as firmly to our thoughts, and this can help us to 1) doubt that our thoughts are always true and 2) relax a bit as that compelling thought becomes less convincing. It is important to note that individuals with trauma histories may find loosening the grip on their thoughts (and their perceived reality) can result in unpleasant flashbacks or other emotional setbacks. As you begin a meditation practice, start slowly with 5 or 10 minutes of sitting. Pay close attention to how you feel. Seek advice from a professional therapist if you experience a flashback or something unexpected occurs.

Countless phone applications proclaim to "teach" meditation. While some meditative techniques may help with relaxation or sleep, they do not address the emotional resilience goal of having strong emotions without being devastated by them. Meditation is not a quick fix like taking a pill when you feel off your emotional game. Most of the techniques to "feel better" will eventually fail as the ego decides "This is not working. It must be bullshit." The "bullshit" starts as you first start to sit for longer periods and notice how uncomfortable it is to not be constantly adjusting your body. The ego generally subscribes to the belief "I should always be comfortable," and this thought may drive you crazy as you resist the urge to scratch a maddening itch on your left ear. The itch, as with many difficult/unpleasant emotions, will gradually calm down and take care of itself if we simply observe it and leave it alone. If we practice nonreactivity to unmet expectations and challenges, we will be better equipped to hold out against suboptimal responses that may make matters worse. For example, when you receive a very upsetting email, it is better to stay with your upset until it cools rather than giving in to the trigger of sending an incendiary reply you will regret.

Meditation isn't a one-size-fits-all tool, and creating a practice that works for you is key. Stay flexible in your approach as it evolves to meet your needs. What you desire to get out of your practice is totally up to you.

EXERCISE 3.5: LEARN TO MEDITATE (SEATED)

- Most people who have grown up in Western culture find it very difficult (painful) to sit on the floor. It is okay to sit in a chair. Postures facilitating seated meditation on the floor can be found at Zmm. org (Zen Mountain Monastery, 2021).

- Sit in a chair, keeping your back straight and your feet flat on the floor so they form a 90-degree angle with your knees. Sitting on the edge of the chair may help with positioning so you don't need to rely on the back of the chair for support (unless you have back issues that need that support).

- Your thighs should be level and parallel to the floor. If your thighs slope up or down, you can adjust the height by using a pillow or small blanket under your posterior or your feet.

- Sit up straight with an alert but relaxed posture. Keep your shoulders relaxed and comfortable, drawing them slightly back and down to keep your back strong and heart center open. If you relax and your back collapses into a "C" shape, you may need to tilt your hips forward in order to position your head and neck in line with your spine. You may place a rolled towel or pillow behind your lower back for added support.

- Rest your hands on your thighs or in your lap (palms up or down).

- Slightly tuck in your chin while maintaining length in the back of your neck.

- Eyes can be open or closed, but decide which way you will meditate before you begin. Switching back and forth between open and closed eyes can disrupt the flow of your meditation. Keep your face, eyes, and eyelids relaxed. If you are really agitated, closing the eyes can help with calming. If you are sleepy, opening the eyes can help to not fall asleep. If your eyes are open, maintain an unfocused gaze at the floor a few feet in front of you.

- Begin with taking two deep, slow breaths, in through the nose and out through the mouth. This is to help relax and center.

- Now begin following your breath. Find a place where you can notice the soft sensation of breath coming and going. Likely places are your nostrils, upper lip, chest, or belly. Do not try to control your breath; let it be. However it is is just fine.

- Your mind will wander from attending to breath sensations. When that happens, smile and gently bring your mind back to the present—to the breath sensations—without judgment (smile is because you are not doing it wrong because your mind wandered but in the instant you notice you have wandered, you can come back, and this is the point).

- Set a timer for 5–10 minutes so you do not have to keep looking at your phone to see if the time is up. Make a commitment to meditate for the duration of the time you signed up for. This practice is hard because the ego hates meditation (you are not "accomplishing" anything), so 5–10 minutes is long enough for the first few months of meditation. Try to meditate daily and find a consistent time that fits into your schedule. Whatever comes up is okay. If you have calm and bliss, you are doing the meditation right. If you have angry, agitated meditation, you are still meditating correctly. There is no wrong way to meditate.

You Do Not Have to Explain

Explaining your story can get in the way of emotional resilience because the act of explaining an emotion invites evaluation of whether the emotion is "valid" or not. Someone explaining to you how to fix your car may be helpful because you might not know how to do the repair, so your knowledge needs to be augmented. When you have an emotion, it is true for you, so the explanation invites someone to try and talk you out of it or causes you to question whether you have "the right" to have that emotion. You are justified in having any emotions that come, as they are a product of your history and current situation, neither of which you can control. You are not justified in reacting to an emotion without reflection. If someone says something that triggers your anger, it is not okay to punch them in the face. However, after you cool off, you may need to address what triggered the anger, either through adjusting your thoughts about the situation (see doubt above) or through maintaining a boundary ("You cannot take my car because I need it tonight").

Rather than explaining ("I have a right to be mad because you ate my food"), it may be effective to disclose your emotional state ("I felt angry when I realized all my cereal was gone") and then to ask for what you need ("Please do not eat my cereal. I will mark my box so you know it is mine"). Disclosing and asking for what you need gives you the best chance of getting help for your difficult emotional state. Sometimes you may not know the right words for disclosing your emotional state. Table 3.3 shows several examples of emotional descriptor words along with their corresponding emotional intensity. A more complete list can be found on the Internet at Tomdrummond.com (2021).

TABLE 3.3 Emotional Words				
Intensity/emotion	Happy	Sad	Scared	Lonely
Strong	Ecstatic	Devastated	Terrified	Abandoned
Medium	Happy	Blue	Scared	Left out
Light	Pleased	A little down	Nervous	Distant

By getting emotionally more mature within the working environment, people realized that they actually had the power within themselves to change things and transform their everyday working life in the most effective way.

—Lemisiou, 2018

Summary

An old Cherokee is teaching his grandson about life. "A fight is going on inside me," he said to the boy. "It is a terrible fight and it is between two wolves. One is evil—he is anger, envy, sorrow, regret, greed, arrogance, self-pity, guilt, resentment, inferiority, lies, false pride, superiority, and ego."

He continued, "The other is good—he is joy, peace, love, hope, serenity, humility, kindness, benevolence, empathy, generosity, truth, compassion, and faith. The same fight is going on inside you—and inside every other person, too."

The grandson thought about it for a minute and then asked his grandfather, "Which wolf will win?" The old Cherokee simply replied, "The one you feed."

—*The Story of Two Wolves*, 2016

Source: https://urbanbalance.com/the-story-of-two-wolves/.

Emotions are like many wolves inside of us. Ruminating on a difficult emotion is like feeding a wolf we might not want around. The fed emotion will grow and take on a life of its own until we react to the intensity by lashing out or doing something we may later regret. Not feeding the wolf does not mean ignoring the wolf. Our emotions have something to tell us. Feeling fear as we see a bus coming toward us in the street is valuable because it motivates us to get out of harm's way. However, if that same fear crops up in rumination while reading a book, we might acknowledge the fear (fear of being hit by a truck) and then return to our book (just like returning to the breath in meditation). As we acknowledge the fear and turn away, the fear of being hit by a truck will gradually lose intensity in situations where it really does not help.

It is important to acknowledge that most of our emotional reactions are born out of our genetics and upbringing. This is not an excuse like "Well, my parents did this to me" but rather a way to recognize that some of our emotional reactions are from old stories that no longer apply. As you recognize your reactions to old stories, smile at them like you would smile at any toddler who is having a difficult time. You can reassure the toddler inside you that this older, adult version of you can handle the situation and that you now have more power and tools than the toddler had. You might even thank the old story as you recognize your mind trying to protect you from repeating earlier hurts.

You can strengthen your ability to cope with difficulties and your emotional responses to them with the exercises in this chapter. Remember:

- Your emotions are not "good" or "bad." They may be pleasant or unpleasant, but be curious about what your emotions have to tell you.

- Social support is one of the most important supports of emotional resilience. Make it a priority to engage in healthy, supportive friendships that you can call on when you are feeling difficult emotions. Consider clubs, church, or volunteering as opportunities to connect with others.

- Emotions last longer when we ruminate about them. The story keeps repeating without any satisfying end. Consider using distancing, distracting, and reappraisal of the situation to move past the ruminative story.

- Work on your emotional vocabulary. The better you get at expressing what is going on for you, the more satisfying responses you will get from others (including support) because you will be better known.

- Try belly breathing for a month. Gradually increase the duration to 2–4 minutes. See how that helps your internal calmness.

- Try meditation for 8 weeks (typical length of time to build a new habit). Notice what comes up as you are distracted from your breath and your mind wanders. Smile, and return to your breath.

- Know which wolf you are feeding. Remember to be loving and gentle with yourself as you evolve this skill.

Sometimes we need extra help to deal with difficult emotions. Emotions can be really strong when you have depression, anxiety, or a trauma background. You might want to enlist a therapist for additional support as you learn coping techniques. Therapists can be counselors, social workers, or psychologists. Additional feeling/body-oriented therapies you might want to explore include:

- EMDR—eye movement desensitization and reprogramming. This is a therapy that can be very helpful for trauma.

- SE—systematic experiencing. This therapy helps people to more fully experience their bodies and develop insight regarding how stories, triggers, and emotions interrelate.

- DSP—developmental somatic psychotherapy. A movement-oriented therapy from Gestalt psychology that uses movement to build insight.

Reflection Questions

1. Inuit parenting is one of the most gentle styles of parenting in the world (National Public Radio, 2019). The Inuit parents believe that reacting to strong emotions like anger is a childish response and is not fitting for an adult. Read the article at Npr.org. Do you feel that avoiding raising one's voice to children is helpful or not? Why?

2. Revisit (or do it for the first time) the value sort exercise from this chapter. Review your top three values and ask "How does this inform the directions I am taking in my life?" Reflect on how you are living in a way that reflects what you value or how your life is not reflective of your values.

3. Notice how your body feels right now. If you notice a strong sensation (tightness, hunger, itch, etc.), ask "What are you here to tell me?" Review the section regarding different "hungers" from this chapter and see if that suggests actions to address the feelings (you may or may not get the answer right away, as this is a practice too).

References

Alegre, A., & Benson, M. J. (2010). Parental behaviors and adolescent adjustment: Mediation via adolescent trait emotional intelligence. *Individual Differences Research, 8*(2), 83–96.

The blue cliff record. (2005). T. Cleary and J. C. Cleary (Trans.). Shambhala Publications.

Centers for Disease Control and Prevention. (2021). *About the CDC-Kaiser ACE study.* https://www.cdc.gov/violenceprevention/aces/about.html

Chang, R. (2014, May). *How to make hard choices.* https://www.ted.com/talks/ruth_chang_how_to_make_hard_choices

Drummond, Tom. *Emotion vocabulary.* (2021). https://tomdrummond.com/leading-and-caring-for-children/emotion-vocabulary/

Felitti, V. J., Anda, R. F., Nordenberg, D., Williamson, D. F., Spitz, A. M., Edwards, V., Koss, M. P., & Marks, J. S. (1998). Relationship of childhood abuse and household dysfunction to many of the leading causes of death in adults. *American Journal of Preventive Medicine, 14*(4), 245–258. https://doi.org/10.1016/S0749-3797(98)00017-8

Flouri, E., Midouhas, E., Joshi, H., & Tzavidis, N. (2015). Emotional and behavioural resilience to multiple risk exposure in early life: The role of parenting. *European Child & Adolescent Psychiatry, 24*(7), 745–755. https://doi.org/10.1007/s00787-014-0619-7

Frank, R. (2001). *Body of awareness: A somatic and developmental approach to psychotherapy.* Gestalt Press.

Frank, R., & La Barre, F. (2010). *The first year and the rest of your life: Movement, development, and psychotherapeutic change.* Routledge.

Frankl, V. E., Goleman, D., Vesely, F., & Young, J. (2019). *Yes to life: In spite of everything.* Boston: Beacon Press.

Katie, B., & Mitchell, S. (2002). *Loving what is: Four questions that can change your life.* Harmony Books.

Lemisiou, M. A. (2018). The effectiveness of person-centered coaching intervention in raising emotional and social intelligence competencies in the workplace. *International Coaching Psychology Review, 13*(2), 6–26.

National Public Radio. (2019, March 13). *How Inuit parents teach kids to control their anger.* https://www.npr.org/sections/goatsandsoda/2019/03/13/685533353/a-playful-way-to-teach-kids-to-control-their-anger

Porges, S. W. (2012). *Neural mechanisms mediating social behaviour and health.* [PESI training materials].

Porges, S. W. (2018) The neurophysiology of trauma, attachment, self-regulation & emotions. (2017). [PESI training materials].

Sarrionandia, A., & Mikolajczak, M. (2020). A meta-analysis of the possible behavioural and biological variables linking trait emotional intelligence to health. *Health Psychology Review, 14*(2), 220–244. https://doi.org/10.1080/17437199.2019.1641423

Urban Balance. *The story of two wolves.* (2016, February 24). https://urbanbalance.com/the-story-of-two-wolves/

van der Kolk, B. A. (2014). *The body keeps the score: Brain, mind, and body in the healing of trauma.* Viking.

Verduyn, P., Delaveau, P., Rotgé, J.-Y., Fossati, P., & Van Mechelen, I. (2015). Determinants of emotion duration and underlying psychological and neural mechanisms. *Emotion Review, 7*(4), 330–335. https://doi.org/10.1177/1754073915590618

Verduyn, P., Delvaux, E., Van Coillie, H., Tuerlinckx, F., & Van Mechelen, I. (2009). Predicting the duration of emotional experience: Two experience sampling studies. *Emotion, 9*(1), 83–91. https://doi.org/10.1037/a0014610

Verduyn, P., & Lavrijsen, S. (2015). Which emotions last longest and why: The role of event importance and rumination. *Motivation and Emotion, 39*(1), 119–127. https://doi.org/10.1007/s11031-014-9445-y

Wright, M. O., & Masten, A. S. (2005). Resilience processes in development. In S. Goldstein & R. B. Brooks (Eds.), *Handbook of resilience in children* (pp. 17–37). Springer Link. https://doi.org/10.1007/0-306-48572-9_2

Yanfeng, W., Zhuo, L., & Liqi, Z. (2019). Emotional intelligence of 3- to 6-year-olds and parenting style: Peer communication ability as a mediator. *Social Behavior & Personality: An International Journal, 47*(12), 1–12. https://doi.org/10.2224/sbp.8636

Zen Mountain Monastery. (2020). *How to meditate: Zazen instructions.* https://zmm.org/teachings-and-training/meditation-instructions/

Credits

CHAPTER 4

Social Resilience

Tyler Hudson, MA

Though one may be overpowered, two can defend themselves. A cord of three strands is not quickly broken.

—Qoheleth

Social Support: An Essential Resilience Factor

For all of its wonders, life is full of distressing realities. A recent scroll through a reputable news app highlighted the following: COVID death rates, racism, murder, political upheaval, climate change, corruption, kidnappings, and terrorism. The hard reality is that life comes with distress and our exposure to it is inevitable. Whether it's on the news and halfway around the world or in our own city, workplace, school, or family, everyone inevitably feels the influence of distress. We can limit stressors and their effects by healthy habits and practices; however, we simply do not have control over every area of our lives and what we're exposed to on a daily basis. So what are we to do? In my clinical practice, I remind my clients that we have both a proactive and a reactive role to play in the management of our wellness. *Reactively,* we can choose how we respond to certain events and, with intentionality and practice, replace maladaptive responses with healthy and constructive reactions. *Proactively*, we can increase our mental toughness, well-being, and resilience. Resilience is "the ability to persist in the face of challenges and to bounce back from adversity" (Luthar, Cicchetti, & Becker, 2000; Reivich, Seligman, & McBride, 2011, p. 25) and is essential to both attaining and maintaining well-being.

Fortunately, we know which factors contribute to resilience and that we can develop this over time. Research tells us that mental toughness, self-efficacy, flexibility, impulse control, attractiveness, empathy, and spirituality all contribute to personal resilience (Masten & Reed, 2002; Truffino, 2010; Werner, 1993). Some factors are buffering—softening the blow of stressors. Others are enhancing—increasing positive aspects of wellness that contribute to grit, and other factors possess both qualities. Although resilience development models vary slightly in their inclusion of some factors, all of the major resilience models include social support as a core resilience aspect in their curriculum, and for good reason.

In this chapter, you'll learn what social support really is, understand how social support contributes to resilience, and identify specific practices that can enhance your own resilience and the resilience of your relationships. We'll identify different aspects of social support that give us the ability to bounce back from hardships, learn how to put these to use, and discover how to strengthen and protect our relationships from succumbing to the pressures of life as well.

Social Support

Social support can be thought of as any information that leads people to believe that they are cared for and loved, esteemed, and a member of a network of reciprocal commitments (Cobb, 1976). Social support involves the meeting of dependency needs without a lost sense of self, shared values and beliefs, and reciprocal behaviors intended to enhance the well-being of the recipient, such as nurturance, recognition and respect, affiliation, and emotional availability (Gore, 1973; Shumaker & Browell, 1984). If you ask a veteran what they miss the most about their service days, they'll likely bring up camaraderie. Those who play sports or belong to a club understand this feeling as well. To most, the experience of connecting with others feels automatic and is explained by what social scientists call the *belongingness hypothesis*, which suggests people naturally form social connections under most conditions and are predisposed to resist the weakening of existing attachments (Baumeister & Leary, 1995).

Structure and Function

Social support involves both structural and functional dimensions. The structural component of social support refers to the size and frequency of social interactions, while the functional component explains the emotional and instrumental components (Ozbay, Johnson, Dimoulas, Morgan, Charney, & Southwick, 2007). Interestingly, but perhaps not surprisingly, research has consistently demonstrated that the quality of relationships has a more predictive and effective influence on resiliency and health than the quantity of relationships (Kiecolt-Glaser & Newton, 2001). Quality matters much more than quantity, which is why people might experience the feeling of loneliness or isolation despite being in a crowded room or having a full contact list. Quality relationships provide us with the intellectual and emotional awareness that we belong. Additionally, quality relationships offer connections within a community that are reliable, available, and adequate to meet certain emotional and practical needs (Barrera, 1986).

The perception of adequacy is a critical component of social support and refers to the provision of both expressive and instrumental support (Gillespie, Lever, Frederick, & Royce, 2015). When you're emotionally available to someone by letting them vent about their day at work, empathize with their experience about going back home for the weekend, or even just actively listen, you're providing them with expressive support. When you take notes for your friend, bring them meals while they're quarantined, or give them a spot at the gym, you're offering instrumental support. Both are valid, and both are needed at different times. It's important to give and receive the type of support needed in that moment. Receiving one when we need the other is like being given a glass of cool water when we're hungry or being given a nice meal when we're actually thirsty. Everyone has had the experience of someone who starts problem-solving (instrumental) when we really need them to listen and empathize (expressive) and vice versa. Typically, as relationships develop, we pick up on cues that indicate what type of support is needed in different moments. In other instances, we simply need to ask, "What would be supportive to you right now?"

If you're interested in enhancing the relationships you currently have, bring someone to mind and answer the following questions:

1. How do they make you feel like you belong?
2. How could you communicate (through word or deed) to them that they belong?
3. What practical ways can you demonstrate reliability within this relationship? Availability? Adequacy? Hint: If you have a hard time identifying some practical steps to demonstrate these traits, reverse engineer it and think about what would demonstrate the opposite trait first (e.g., unreliable, unavailable, inadequate).
4. Are you more likely to offer expressive or instrumental social support? Set an intention to practice offering the type that doesn't come as naturally or even asking what they need more from you in a moment.
5. What cues do they give you that indicate they need some emotional support? Practical support?

Social Support and Resiliency

Research over the last three decades shows social support protects and enhances our overall health. Our own personal experience reminds us that a quality relationship is a good thing to have and a detrimental thing to lack (Thoits, 2011). There are significant emotional, physiological, and behavioral outcomes when we feel socially supported and devastating consequences when our relationships are threatened or nonexistent. We can think of the benefits as both *buffering* and *enhancing*. That is to say that social support protects us from the full effects of ordinary daily stressors as well as acute, traumatic, and negative experiences and averts the negative outcomes of perceived social isolation. Social support also independently provides positive or enhancing benefits as a main effect (see Figure 4.1).

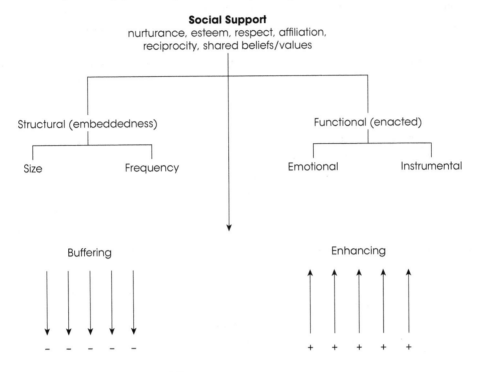

FIGURE 4.1   Social Support and Components

Buffering

Generally, we experience stress when we perceive that a demand outweighs our perceived capability. This experience taxes self-esteem and contributes to feelings of helplessness and ultimately to illness through prolonged sympathetic activation (Sapolsky, 2004). Simply put, our body isn't meant to be in a state of chronic stress and exposure to cortisol. Social support buffers this experience by providing individuals with the awareness that others could step in to assist with the perceived threat or demand, thereby altering the perception of possible harm or risk. Additionally, social support may intervene during the stress reaction by assisting with the cognitive appraisal of the demand or outcome or by providing possible solutions (Cohen & Wills, 1985). Buffering occurs when the perceived provision reasonably matches the perceived need (see Figure 4.2).

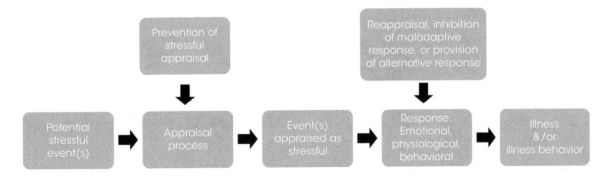

FIGURE 4.2   Points at which social support may intervene along the causal link between stress and illness. Adapted from Cohen & Wills, 1985.

Social support has been shown to buffer against the effects of trauma, academic stress, and mood disorders (Prati & Pietrantoni, 2009; Vogel, Wade, Wester, Larson, & Hackler, 2007; Wilks, 2008). Among veterans of the Operation Enduring Freedom and Iraqi Freedom (OEF/OIF) campaigns, those who had strong social support reported less post-traumatic stress, fewer depressive symptoms, and greater positive outcomes arising from trauma, known as post-traumatic growth (PTG; Pietrzak, Johnson, Goldstein, Malley, & Southwick, 2009).

Social support not only prevents stressors from worsening but also prevents specific negative outcomes from originating. The lack of social support has been termed *perceived social isolation* and refers to the experience of loneliness and a perceived lack of communal sustenance and provision (Cornwell & Waite, 2009). Evolutionary biologists tell us that the discomfort experienced as a result of the social pain of loneliness has multiple purposes and evolutionary utility. Behavioral studies as well as fMRI studies indicate social isolation increases attention to negative social stimuli and produces discomfort (Cacioppo, Hawkley, Norman, & Berntson, 2011). This discomfort is a "signal" that connections, historically essential to our survival, are weakening and serve as a motivator to repair and maintain these relationships for the evolutionary purpose of maintaining our genes (Cacioppo et al., 2011). A persistent sense of estrangement or isolation increases the risk of mood disorders, suicide, and substance abuse (McWhirter, 1990). The effects of loneliness have prompted an abundance of research, particularly among older adults, who comprise one of the fastest-growing demographics in the United States (Cacioppo & Hawkley, 2003). Those who are socially isolated experience higher levels of anxiety, negative moods, hostility, fear of negative evaluation, and perceived stress, lower levels of optimism, happiness, and life satisfaction, and even an increase in wound-healing time (Cacioppo & Hawkley, 2003; Cacioppo, Hawkley, Crawford, Ernst, Burleson, Kowalewski, Malarkey, Cauter, & Berntson, 2002). In fact, when compared to smoking, obesity, sedentary lifestyle, and high blood pressure, social isolation was as strong a risk factor for morbidity and mortality (Cacioppo et al., 2011; House, Landis, & Umberson, 1988).

Enhancing

Social support not only reduces the negative emotional, behavioral, and physiological effects of stressors but has a positive influence on these processes as well. Social support assists with blood pressure regulation, reduces cardiovascular reactivity due to acute stress, regulates the endocrine system (e.g., cortisol secretion), and improves immune system functioning (Uchino, Cacioppo, & Kiecolt-Glaser, 1996). The emotional and behavioral effects are just as significant. Social support provides individuals with resources to turn to when things go poorly but also when things go well. A social support system provides us with a community that can celebrate our accomplishments and positive experiences. Usually, when something goes well (e.g., a good grade on an exam or getting into college or grad school), our first inclination is to tell someone we care about. When we do this, we actually increase our positive affect and well-being beyond that which is provided by the event itself. These benefits are enhanced even further when we get a positive response from the person we shared with, increasing intimacy and relational satisfaction (Gable, Reis, Impett, & Asher, 2004).

Sources of Social Support

Friends and Significant Others

Primary sources of social support include family, friends, and significant others or partners. Although men have historically reported less social support from friends and significant others, a recent national study of over 25,000 participants (Gillespie, Lever, Frederick, & Royce, 2015) found very little difference between men and women across subgroups. Regardless of the definition of "friend" that was used, men and women reported similar numbers of friends irrespective of age, marital status, and parental status. This number tends to decrease as we age due to the death of close friends and health limitations that make it difficult to get together. The number of close friends also tends to decrease beginning in our 30s and 40s due to a "pruning effect" (Carstensen, 2006), which describes the common process of limiting the number of friends within our social network into smaller and more intimate clusters.

Family

It is difficult to overestimate the buffering and enhancing effects of the family on resilience, particularly among children. In fact, the home environment and family are the greatest predictors of resilience among adolescents, which we all once identified as, followed by community and peer environments (Dias & Cadime, 2017). Family is where we create initial attachments, learn how to regulate our emotions, receive crucial resources and opportunities, and learn how to adapt to adverse situations (Crowley & Kazdin, 1998; Masten & Shaffer, 2006; Masten, Morison, Pellegrini, & Tellegen, 1992). Although this is critical during our younger years, it's also important as we age. Healthy families provide a "home base" to return to and orient us to reality and healthy ways of being.

As you bring your family of origin to mind, consider the following questions:

1. What benefits did your family social support system provide you with?
2. Who was the first person you contacted the last time you were celebrating something?
3. Who did you reach out to when something went poorly?
4. How did they make you feel when you did? And how could you meaningfully communicate that to them?

Social Media

Our intrinsic desire for relationships makes the allure of social media predictable. Social media offers immediate access to a broader social support system than we might have otherwise. The ability to converse and share media with virtually anyone in the world at any time provides opportunities for social support that are unprecedented in both expressive and instrumental ways. However, as we know, the negative effects of social media are real, too. Although we have greater access to a broader support system than ever before, we also have greater exposure to bullying, violence, suicidal and non-suicidal self-injury ideation and encouragement, and more. This negative exposure, along with Internet addiction and concurrent sleep deprivation, ironically often leaves us feeling more socially isolated than supported. Social media use produces a paradoxical phenomenon of both supplying social support, a significant predictor of resilience and well-being, while simultaneously influencing the holistic health of individuals in severely negative ways. Unsurprisingly, social media consumption is correlated with increased levels of depression and anxiety, decreased self-esteem, and poor sleep quality (Lin, Sidani, Shensa, Radovic, Miller, Colditz, Hoffman, Giles, & Primack, 2016; Woods & Scott, 2016).

It might be helpful to think of our social media consumption in the same way that we think of our dietary intake. We don't eat or drink indiscriminately if we want to be or remain healthy. Similarly, we don't "consume" any and all types of social media without regulation if we want to be mentally well. What are some limits you could voluntarily put on your social media consumption? What does a healthy "diet" look like for you? You might consider the following:

1. Limit the amount of time you spend on social media each day. You could start by setting aside an hour when you avoid it completely and see how you feel. Or, if you're feeling up for a challenge and think it would be beneficial, delete it from your phone for a week as a kind of social media "fast."
2. Observe your mood after you spend any amount of time using social media. How do you feel after you close the app?
3. Avoid social media at least one hour before bedtime and don't keep your phone in your room at night to avoid sleep disruption.
4. Remove the social media apps from your phone to create a mindful pause before jumping onto an app out of habit. Having to log on through a browser can give you enough time to determine if this is going to be beneficial or detrimental.

Resilient Relationships

The vital roles that others play in our resilience and well-being mean that it's important to also increase the strength of our relationships. As we've noted, the quality of our relationships is much more important than how many we have. Like anything else that's good for us, relationships take sustained effort and work. So how can we strengthen our relationships? Consider adopting some of the following evidence-based suggestions:

1. Practice healthy communication skills:

   a. Take turns and fully listen to the other before responding.
   b. Practice active listening by restating what the other person said and reflecting on their feelings.
   c. Avoid using the word "you" and turn it into an "I" statement. We usually quit listening and get defensive once we hear "you" uttered in an accusatory way.
      i. "You" statement: "You never do the dishes around here! I'm always picking up your messes, and I'm tired of it."
      ii. "I" statement: "When I come home and see the dishes in the sink, it makes me feel like my time isn't valued."
   d. Practice perspective taking. The renowned relationship experts John and Julie Gottman refer to this as the Rapoport technique. Whenever you think about something you've done that you feel proud of, commit to bringing to mind instances when your friend or partner has done the same thing. Similarly, whenever you think about something your friend or partner has done that you find upsetting, commit to asking yourself if or when you've done something similar. This also helps cultivate gratitude, which further strengthens your relationships.

2. Establish routines around spending time together. I recently heard a father say he doesn't spend a lot of time with his kids but he does spend quality time with them. This isn't how it works. Quality time comes from a quantity of time, and whoever said that time is the currency of love was right.

3. Know what to avoid as well. Just like we avoid certain foods or behaviors if we want to be physically healthy, we should avoid certain pitfalls with relationships if we want them and ourselves to be resilient and well.

   a. Don't avoid boundaries—Boundaries tell others where their influence stops and are an essential ingredient in healthy relationships.
   b. Don't accept personal myths—I hear a lot of men in particular speak of themselves as lone wolves. Healthy independence is a good thing, but we're interdependent, and as we've seen, research shows that we don't do well when we're isolated and don't feel socially supported.
   c. Don't misinterpret conflict—Conflict is a healthy aspect of any relationship. The key is how conflict is done: constructive and healthy conflict versus destructive and counterproductive conflict full of accusations, name calling, criticism, and refusing to accept influence from another.
   d. Don't handle conflict too soon or too late—Conflict should be discussed when both parties are in a neutral or positive emotional state. When we escalate emotionally, we can count on conflict going poorly. Consider picking a time at least a half hour from when the conflict occurred. If that isn't possible, try not to let a week go by without discussing the state of the relationship and making effective repairs.

The need for social support has perhaps never been more apparent. A year of sheltering in place, social distancing, and not making plans that we usually take for granted has reminded all of us of our need to be in relationships and in proximity to others. Being cut off from others, for whatever reason, has deleterious effects on our mental and physical health and causes us to feel the full weight of certain stressors. Having quality relationships, as we have seen, not only cushions the blow but also enhances our lives in every domain. In light of this, we need to invest in our healthy relationships as if our well-being depends on it. Some of these suggestions will work for you, and others might require some modification—that's okay. If we prioritize being in healthy relationships and working to maintain them, we reap the benefits of social support, which includes increasing our resiliency.

Social Wellness and Resiliency Tips

1. Prioritize social support and time with healthy others.
2. Remember that social support is both expressive and instrumental.
3. Spend time strengthening your relationships.
4. Relationships take work.
5. Social support doesn't always mean face to face.
6. Social support communicates belonging and is both buffering and enhancing.
7. The quality of relationships matters more than the quantity of relationships.
8. Not all social interactions are socially supportive.
9. Loneliness is correlated with mood disorders and disruption.
10. Social support both prevents stressors from worsening and prevents certain stressors from originating.

Reflection Questions

1. What are your automatic thoughts related to social support?
2. What could you do to strengthen the relationships you currently have?
3. What kind of support do you find yourself benefiting from most often (e.g., expressive or instrumental)?
4. What traps do you fall into that inhibit your social support and resilience?

References

Barrera, M., Jr. (1986). Distinctions between social support concepts, measures, and models. *American Journal of Community Psychology, 14*(4), 413–445.

Baumeister, R. F., & Leary, M. R. (1995). The need to belong: Desire for interpersonal attachments as a fundamental human motivation. *Psychological Bulletin, 117*(3), 497.

Cacioppo, J. T., & Hawkley, L. C. (2003). Social isolation and health, with an emphasis on underlying mechanisms. *Perspectives in Biology and Medicine, 46*(3), S39–S52.

Cacioppo, J. T., Hawkley, L. C., Crawford, L. E., Ernst, J. M., Burleson, M. H., Kowalewski, R. B., Malarkey, W. B., Cauter, E. V., & Berntson, G. G. (2002). Loneliness and health: Potential mechanisms. *Psychosomatic Medicine, 64*(3), 407–417.

Cacioppo, J. T., Hawkley, L. C., Norman, G. J., & Berntson, G. G. (2011). Social isolation. *Annals of the New York Academy of Sciences, 1231*(1), 17–22.

Carstensen, L. L. (2006). The influence of a sense of time on human development. *Science, 312*(5782), 1913–1915.

Cohen, S., & Wills, T. A. (1985). Stress, social support, and the buffering hypothesis. *Psychological Bulletin, 98*(2), 310.

Cornwell, E. Y., & Waite, L. J. (2009). Social disconnectedness, perceived isolation, and health among older adults. *Journal of Health and Social Behavior, 50*(1), 31–48.

Crowley, M. J., & Kazdin, A. E. (1998). Child psychosocial functioning and parent quality of life among clinically referred children. *Journal of Child and Family Studies, 7*(2), 233–251.

Dias, P. C., & Cadime, I. (2017). Protective factors and resilience in adolescents: The mediating role of self-regulation. *Psicología Educativa, 23*(1), 37–43.

Gable, S. L., Reis, H. T., Impett, E. A., & Asher, E. R. (2004). What do you do when things go right? The intrapersonal and interpersonal benefits of sharing positive events. *Journal of Personality and Social Psychology, 87*(2), 228.

Gillespie, B. J., Lever, J., Frederick, D., & Royce, T. (2015). Close adult friendships, gender, and the life cycle. *Journal of Social and Personal Relationships, 32*(6), 709–736.

Gore, S. (1974). *The influence of social support and related variables in ameliorating the consequences of job loss.* (Doctoral dissertation, ProQuest Information & Learning).

House, J. S., Landis, K. R., & Umberson, D. (1988). Social relationships and health. *Science, 241*(4865), 540–545.

Kiecolt-Glaser, J. K., & Newton, T. L. (2001). Marriage and health: His and hers. *Psychological Bulletin, 127,* 472–503.

Lin, L. Y., Sidani, J. E., Shensa, A., Radovic, A., Miller, E., Colditz, J. B., Hoffman, B. L., Giles, L. M., & Primack, B. A. (2016). Association between social media use and depression among US young adults. *Depression and Anxiety, 33*(4), 323–331.

Luthar, S. S., Cicchetti, D., & Becker, B. (2000). The construct of resilience: A critical evaluation and guidelines for future work. *Child Development, 71*(3), 543–562.

Masten, A. S., & Reed, M. G. J. (2002). Resilience in development. *Handbook of Positive Psychology, 74,* 88.

Masten, A. S., & Shaffer, A. (2006). How families matter in child development: Reflections from research on risk and resilience. In A. Clarke-Stewart & J. Dunn (Eds.), *Families count: Effects on child and adolescent development* (pp. 5–25). Cambridge University Press.

Masten, A., Morison, P., Pellegrini, D., & Tellegen, A. (1990). Competence under stress: Risk and protective factors. In J. Rolf, A. Masten, D. Cicchetti, K. Nüchterlein, & S. Weintraub (Eds.), *Risk and protective factors in the development of psychopathology* (pp. 236–256). Cambridge University Press. doi:10.1017/CBO9780511752872.015

McWhirter, B. T. (1990). Loneliness: A review of current literature, with implications for counseling and research. *Journal of Counseling & Development, 68*(4), 417–422.

Ozbay, F., Johnson, D. C., Dimoulas, E., Morgan III, C. A., Charney, D., & Southwick, S. (2007). Social support and resilience to stress: From neurobiology to clinical practice. *Psychiatry, 4*(5), 35.

Pearson, J. E. (1986). The definition and measurement of social support. *Journal of Counseling & Development, 64*(6), 390–395. https://doi.org/10.1002/j.1556-6676.1986.tb01144.x

Pietrzak, R. H., Johnson, D. C., Goldstein, M. B., Malley, J. C., & Southwick, S. M. (2009). Psychological resilience and postdeployment social support protect against traumatic stress and depressive symptoms in soldiers returning from Operations Enduring Freedom and Iraqi Freedom. *Depression and Anxiety, 26*(8), 745–751.

Prati, G., & Pietrantoni, L. (2009). Optimism, social support, and coping strategies as factors contributing to post-traumatic growth: A meta-analysis. *Journal of Loss and Trauma, 14*(5), 364–388.

Reivich, K. J., Seligman, M. E., & McBride, S. (2011). Master resilience training in the US Army. *American Psychologist, 66*(1), 25.

Sapolsky, R. M. (2004). *Why zebras don't get ulcers: The acclaimed guide to stress, stress-related diseases, and coping.* Holt Paperbacks.

Shumaker, S. A., & Brownell, A. (1984). Toward a theory of social support: Closing conceptual gaps. *Journal of Social Issues, 40*(4), 11–36.

Thoits, P. A. (2011). Mechanisms linking social ties and support to physical and mental health. *Journal of Health and Social Behavior, 52*(2), 145–161.

Truffino, J. C. (2010). Resilience: An approach to the concept. *Revista de Psiquiatría y Salud Mental (English Edition), 3*(4), 145–151.

Uchino, B. N. (2009). Understanding the links between social support and physical health: A life-span perspective with emphasis on the separability of perceived and received support. *Perspectives on Psychological Science, 4*(3), 236–255.

Vogel, D. L., Wade, N. G., Wester, S. R., Larson, L., & Hackler, A. H. (2007). Seeking help from a mental health professional: The influence of one's social network. *Journal of Clinical Psychology, 63*(3), 233–245.

Werner, E. E. (1993). Risk, resilience, and recovery: Perspectives from the Kauai Longitudinal Study. *Development and Psychopathology, 5*(4), 503–515.

Wilks, S. E. (2008). Resilience amid academic stress: The moderating impact of social support among social work students. *Advances in Social Work, 9*(2), 106–125.

Woods, H. C., & Scott, H. (2016). #Sleepyteens: Social media use in adolescence is associated with poor sleep quality, anxiety, depression and low self-esteem. *Journal of Adolescence, 51,* 41–49.

Credit

CHAPTER 5

Building Career Resilience

Ana C. Berríos Allison, PhD, LPC

Start by doing what is necessary, then what is possible,
and suddenly you are doing the impossible.

—Francis of Assisi

Career resilience can be understood as your ability to respond to career uncertainty, stress, and decision-making challenges. This dynamic process includes your capacity to adjust, take risks, and recover from planned and unplanned circumstances. Resilience is an ability to bounce back from experiences and move forward, learning about yourself with new meaning.

Being resilient means you can accept your losses and celebrate your accomplishments. Being resilient supports your well-being. You can learn how to be resilient so you can look at your shortcomings and strengths and welcome them as opportunities for personal growth.

You can learn how to be resilient and how to practice resiliency skills. Why can some students change academic majors and adjust while others cannot? What makes some students pick themselves up after a rejection and start the job search process all over again? What makes some students able to deal with an adverse work environment and continue working? What makes some students find meaning in their careers and feel they can contribute to society while others cannot?

Resilient people practice several key skills: persistence, adaptability, and risk-taking. These skills support the many positive transitions and changes you will make regarding your career. Choosing a major and weighing your postgraduate options or accepting a new position and relocating to a new city are just some of the situations that demand persistence, adaptability, and assessing and taking risks.

Characteristics of High and Low Resiliency

We each have individual qualities that facilitate our resiliency. Some students hold a genetic predisposition to be more resilient than others, but we can all learn how to enhance our resiliency. Highly resilient students display self-confidence, determination, and a positive attitude in life. Their capacities for persistence, delayed gratification, and creativity help them communicate well and tackle changing situations.

Additionally, highly resilient students have learned how to control their emotions, think productively, and take risks, which supports them in tolerating and adapting effectively to difficult and stressful situations. They know that laughter relieves stress and compassion helps them respond appropriately to their needs and the needs of others.

Less resilient students define themselves by their stories of rejection and their inability to make choices. They believe they are not capable of making responsible and satisfactory choices. They tend to lack confidence and practice in solving problems productively. Less resilient students tend to have a negative and rigid outlook on life. They will try to appear strong in the face of adversity by asking for little to no help when they need it. As a result, they have learned how to be inflexible and the victim of circumstances.

But there is hope! You can learn better and more resilient skills.

Let's Test Your Career Resilience

The COVID-19 pandemic has brought new career challenges to college students. With classes moved online, many students have found it difficult to manage different faculty expectations. Feeling isolated and without the social supports of the typical college experience, some students are questioning their fit with their academic majors. Others lost their work-study jobs when many university services went virtual. Pandemic-related restrictions during the summer have limited students' opportunities to add value to their resumes or gain income through jobs and internships. The continuation of remote learning is affecting students' ability to connect with professors and networks. The remote college experience is affecting students' participation in extracurricular activities, which are important markers of a college experience and opportunities to develop transferable skills. As a result, many students are questioning the value of their current education and whether it is worth the tuition investment.

Ask Yourself: During the health pandemic, what individual qualities did you develop or practice that demonstrate your resilience? How would these qualities assist you in navigating your career goals?

The uncertainty of life after college can also be anxiety provoking. College students are concerned about their future economic prospects. The job market is uncertain, and many students need to pay back college loans and support themselves. However, it is wise for students to remember that transitioning to the world of work as new professionals always creates some anxieties. All career seekers need to assert their skills, motivation, and fit with new employers and deal with the rejections as part of the job search process. The pandemic has not changed these fundamental parts of the career process. In fact, for the student practicing resiliency, the pandemic may bring new opportunities for career pathways and for developing core transferable skills that employers look for.

Building Career Resilience Through Skills

In today's world, career resilience is no longer just a "nice to have." Career resilience is a core professional competency. Being adaptable, self-initiating, and collaborative are among the key qualities of highly resilient individuals. These are also the qualities employers look for in their employees. You can't control the job market or the decisions an employer will make, but you *can* control how you develop and demonstrate these qualities. By focusing your attention on key career skills that you can control, you will simultaneously build career resilience, inner strength, and a positive attitude toward life and its challenges and opportunities.

You are not in this alone. Career services at your college can assist you in maximizing your career resilience. Take advantage of these professionals. They want to work with you. Plus, you have already paid for their services with your tuition dollars! Career services professionals will encourage you to take risks in life, to understand the value of compromising (and when to compromise and when not to), and to know when to let go of a plan or idea. Finally, building these skills will help you learn how and when to reach out and ask for help. It's good to know that no one can do everything by themselves.

Career experts say the following skills and activities are key for career resilience. Developing these will help you learn more about yourself so you can communicate who you are and what you have to offer with confidence and determination.

- Identifying transferable skills
- Writing resumes and cover letters and learning interviewing skills
- Creating your personal branding
- Negotiating skills
- Building your network

Identifying Transferable Skills

Many of the qualities of highly resilient individuals are what employers call "transferable skills." Transferable skills, as opposed to technical ones, are those skills that are not limited to specific academic disciplines, areas of knowledge, or job tasks. They are universally sought by employers and even graduate/professional schools. Some examples of transferable skills are communication, adaptability, flexibility, confidence, teamwork, creativity, problem-solving, perseverance, risk taking, leadership, diversity, dependability, service, and many others.

Transferable skills are sometimes called "soft skills," but they are anything but soft. They are useful in any work situation and can be acquired outside the classroom. Consider your activities and interests outside academics. What skills have you developed through them? Perhaps you had to research the best way to finance your college education and found that you enjoyed gathering information and figuring out the best way forward. Perhaps you identified a need in your community and marshalled your network to help. Getting involved in cocurricular activities, leadership, athletic experiences, ROTC, study abroad, service learning, part-time and on-campus jobs, and volunteering are just some of the ways you can develop transferable skills.

Your transferable skills—together with your technical ones—will portray you as a well-rounded applicant who can add value to a work environment. Your transferable skills add detail and language to your resume. They also demonstrate your skills and self-knowledge during a job interview. For example, a student who is a member of a university club had the responsibility to set up a table to publicize the club's mission and recruit new students during the annual involvement fair. Through this activity, this student developed and practiced organizational, communication, and interpersonal skills. These are transferable skills the student can highlight in their cover letter and resume as well as during an interview.

> **TIP**
>
> You already have many examples of your transferable skills. Sometimes it's hard for a person to identify their transferable skills and the activities that show those skills in action.
> Talking to a career professional or a good friend will help you articulate them.

Writing Resumes and Cover Letters and Practicing Interviewing Skills

Learning to communicate in writing, on professional social media platforms, and orally are essential parts of the career process. Working on them builds your resilience. They are excellent opportunities to express who you are and what you bring to an employer. You can convey your skills, interests, and narratives about yourself and what matters in life. You can describe what brought you to where you are today, and you can demonstrate your technical and transferable skills with concrete examples. You can convey your motivation and let an employer know how you fit with workplace culture. You can tell them how your performance will add value to their mission. You can express how their vision and values resonate with yours. When an interviewer asks you, "Tell me about yourself," "Tell me about your strengths," or "Tell me about your areas of growth," these typical interview questions are an invitation for you to communicate the fruit of your reflections: your self-knowledge.

Ask Yourself: Let's go back to the question where you were asked to identify individual qualities that demonstrated your career resilience during the health pandemic. You may have already realized that those qualities are some of your transferable skills. Choose one and write a few notes about how this skill could be transferable to your future employment.

Career services can assist you by coaching you through the process of writing resumes and cover letters, preparing a professional on-line presence, and interviewing. Career professionals can support you in preparing a unique strategy to communicate your skills, knowledge, and experiences to an employer and to articulate how you fit with their culture and mission. The process of selecting your skills and qualities that fit the most with potential employers will help you create a confident personal and professional image.

Equally important, career professionals can help you prepare your "stories," short narrative examples that illustrate your technical and transferable skills. By choosing your stories carefully, you can emphasize what you can offer to an employer in a way that is unique to you.

TIPS

1. Undergo mock interviews to practice how you will handle interview questions and how you will articulate your stories that illustrate your skills. Mock interviews will build your confidence in communicating your answers and knowledge of yourself.

2. Tailor your resume and cover letters to each job opening you apply for. Get feedback on your content and format from career professionals, friends, or someone from your network.

LET'S PRACTICE!

The **SAR** technique—**S**cenario, **A**ct, **R**esult—is a technique that helps you back up your statements about your qualifications with concrete examples. The SAR technique gives you a sense of control. Here's how to do it: 1) Choose one skill that you are proud of. 2) Think of one of your experiences that demonstrate that skill: What was the **S**cenario (situation)? How did you **A**ct? What was the **R**esult? 3) Put that SAR information together in one sentence and practice it out loud. 4) Tell the employer. You have now shown how your skill can add value to the company.

Creating Your Personal Branding

Your career is yours alone to manage, and you are responsible for thinking like an entrepreneur. You will need to create your personal brand so it is ready to go when needed. While creating your branding, remember that you are also practicing creativity and problem-solving, two skills that are part of career resiliency.

Career development professionals are in a unique position to assist you with creating your branding. Your branding will help you articulate your value. Branding involves pulling together all your skills, knowledge, and experiences into one unique professional package you can use for successful professional interactions. Your personal brand is your "X factor" that differentiates you from others and makes you indispensable.

It's important that you expand your personal branding to your online presence. For professional purposes, LinkedIn and Twitter are the most important platforms. Create a professional profile that demonstrates your skills and accomplishments. These professional platforms allow you to follow others who share your interests and to keep up with their news and the articles they may publish. It's important to post your thoughts and comments in a professional manner and express your thanks for those who respond to you. Your posts are part of your personal branding and portray your personality and authenticity. Stay diligent about monitoring your online information.

Lastly, prepare your 1-minute commercial. This is a concise self-introduction statement you will have at the ready for any situation: during an interview, when you meet potential coworkers as part of an interview, etc. Be clear and concise. Highlight the most important elements of your personal brand: what you're studying, your key experiences, what you hope to do in the future. Practice, practice, and practice your self-introduction 1-minute commercial. You will quickly see how often you will use it during interviews, job fairs, and other networking events. You will find that your self-introduction will set up your interactions in a positive way. Deliver your introduction, and then let the conversation flow from there.

TIP

Put together a strong career portfolio and have it ready to help showcase who you are and what you offer. Your portfolio will help communicate your skills and abilities with concrete examples that will support your competencies.

LET'S PRACTICE!

Imagine you are at a job fair, either face to face or a virtual event. How would you approach an employer you are interested in? What would you do if a recruiter was interested in you? What would you tell them? This is the time for your 1-minute commercial!

To get started, fill in the blanks:

My name is _____, and I'm a _____ major at _____. I'm interested in _____. My understanding is that your company is _____. As you can see in my enclosed resume, I can offer you _____, _____, _____, and _____ (may add transferable skill) that will make us a great fit.

Negotiating Skills

Learning to negotiate is another skill that will help you build resilience in your career and your life.

Career services can teach you how to negotiate your professional value, salary, and benefits. Negotiating requires that you follow some simple steps. First, gather reliable information about yourself to support your value. As you identify your strong points, enjoy the boost to your confidence and self-esteem. Second, research your employer and learn if salary is negotiable in the first place. Assess the risks of communicating, in assertive ways, what your value add is for the company. Third, offer alternatives realizing how to compromise, looking for the common ground that is beneficial for both the employer and yourself.

By learning the principles of negotiating, you are also learning how to compromise and solve conflict. These are skills that resilient people have; they are also transferable skills. When you need to resolve differences in the workplace or in your personal life, you can apply the same negotiating steps that have you consider different ideas and alternatives. Learning to negotiate effectively also involves learning how to regulate your emotions, keeping them in check so you do not say or do things you might regret later. To control strong emotions, like anger or anxiety, you may need to apply your skills in how to rethink a challenging situation. Accepting with grace and dignity that not all of what you want in life will be achieved is an important aspect of learning how to cope.

Ask Yourself: Could you give an example of when you needed to compromise? What was that like for you? How did you cope?

TIP

Career services can assist you in building this skill by helping you explore the value you will bring to an employment position. Career professionals can also role-play with you in different negotiating scenarios. Through these activities, you will learn how to read the other person and the situation, how to state your worth in ways they will be able to hear, and how to compromise.

Having a solid awareness of who you are, what your best assets are, and what you are willing to sacrifice also reflect your adaptability skills and resiliency. It is important that you know what your nonnegotiables are so you do not take a position or negotiate something that will damage your integrity.

Networking Skills

The art of networking is an important career skill that will help you build and maintain professional relationships. Highly resilient individuals reach out to others to problem solve, to give and ask for help when needed, and to build trusting relationships. Through informational interviews, face-to-face and virtual events (e.g., career fairs, employers' information sessions, professional conferences), and online networking (e.g., LinkedIn), you can learn how to interact with professionals and give and ask for advice. Your network can assist you as you explore academic majors and career options, learn about employers or grad/professional schools, and conduct your job/internship search.

Career services can help you identify the resources you need to sustain your resilience. The resources you use and develop will be different depending on what your needs—professional and personal—are at the time. Networking is a key part of identifying resources. Your contacts will know about resources that you do not. Having a strong network means you can access the information your contacts have: you don't have to know it all!

It is useful to identify your contacts as either warm or cold. Both are useful. Family, friends, and loved ones are your warm contacts. Warm contacts provide natural support systems that will celebrate your career successes and support you during your career difficulties. They can help you bounce back from failures and learn more about yourself when making significant choices, such as in your career.

Cold contacts are people you know but not in as familiar a way. Cold contacts include people you encounter as you go about your academics, internships, work, and other activities. Cold contacts help you expand your access to resources and build your professional network. Let them be a part of your support system. For instance, you may want to build and maintain new relationships on and off campus. Faith-based communities, academic and student life offices, student organizations, faculty, staff, alumni, and classmates are wonderful ways to get connected and feel supported. Your responsibility is to become knowledgeable and informed about these different resources. Career services can teach you how to network and conduct informational interviews, identify contacts, and network at career and academic events.

Be aware that wherever you go, you can express your appreciation regularly to those around you. Let your colleagues know you value them for who they are and what they bring to the organization. Building and maintaining stronger relationships with your coworkers will also ensure you have a support system at and away from work as well as a positive work environment.

TIP

Networking is a wonderful career skill that teaches you the value of relying on one another. Your social support network will help you build trusting relationships you can rely on for support and that can inspire you during losses, disappointments, and hard times. Who are the individuals you trust most in your warm contacts? What makes them so special? Who do you need to reach out to in order to learn more about your next steps in your career?

Let's Review!

We have looked over five career skills that will build your resilience as you take control of your career development. By learning about your transferable skills, writing career documents and interviewing, creating your personal branding, acquiring negotiation skills, and building your professional network, you will practice personal resilience. You will learn how to identify your strengths and areas of growth and how to communicate them creatively and confidently, being aware at all times of your value to the employer.

Resilience gives you a framework of operation to negotiate differences and similarities in professional and dignified ways. A resilient person builds and maintains professional relationships, offering assistance when needed and asking for help when needed. Resilience is learned, practiced, and strengthened.

Ask Yourself: Take some time to consider how you can create a resilient career strategy that will serve you throughout your life. What considerations are most important to you? Why?

The Importance of Decision-Making

When approaching your career decision-making, you need to be planful, strategic, and resilient. Likewise, you need to be open-minded and flexible to expect the unexpected and be comfortable sitting with the ambiguity and uncertainty of life.

As you build up your inner strength and regulate your thoughts, emotions, and behaviors, you will build resilience in your career and other aspects of your life. Being resilient teaches you that life and decision-making are not perfect. You need to learn to anticipate the uncertainty of decision-making and the world of work. You can reframe challenges, setbacks, and the randomness of career paths as opportunities. And yet, even in the face of challenges, remember that you still hold the freedom and power to decide. Should you take a job or hold off? Should you address a problem at work or wait until a more opportune time?

Decision-making is the gift of life for your life. Remember that you have the power to decide many things, including your professional identity.

Challenges can be opportunities to learn about yourself, act on your intentions, and recognize "butterfly moments" in your personal and professional life. Your career and personal paths will sometimes require you to make the most out of strange and interesting happenstances. Chance could help turn your intentions into promising opportunities you will need to act upon. An important component of a resilient person is the ability to distinguish when and how to take risks in the face of uncertainty. They need to trust that they do not need to know all consequences of a potential decision. Sometimes you simply have to realize that it is okay not to know precisely what is next. Centering on your intentions as opposed to your defined career goals can create "wise wanderings" to assist you in your next career move. To succeed in this approach, you must keep your intention in mind and be ready to take action when opportunities appear. You will need to seek your "butterfly moments."

LET'S PRACTICE

This exercise stems from the idea that the tiny atmospheric changes caused by the flap of a butterfly's wings can ultimately have major effects on the course of the weather. Identifying your intentions and following them are the equivalent of the butterfly flapping its wings. The consequences of taking these small steps can be enormous.

I intend to _____

I am seeking _____

I am developing _____

I am creating _____

I am in the process of _____

What could you do in the next 24 hours to move forward with your experimental wanderings, or chase the butterfly? If you knew you couldn't fail, what would you do?

Katharine Brooks (2017) recommends creating an intention box—a compilation of images that attract your interest. The website Pinterest is an ideal online tool to create this type of visual compilation. This visual exercise could be very helpful, particularly if you are feeling a little stuck. Even though you do not have all the answers, you will be much better positioned to engage in "wise wandering" and chase your butterflies trusting your intentions.

Every career path is somewhat circuitous. I challenge you to ask people in your network if they are doing jobs and/or have the careers they planned on when they left college. Very likely the answer will be "no." This doesn't mean their career is a failure or they chose the wrong major. What their "no" highlights is the randomness of opportunity and changes to career paths throughout life. If career change is not always planned; if almost 70% of people say a chance event significantly changed their careers; and if 100% assert they have had a chance event in their careers, what does this mean to you? I hope you see that success depends on your resilience, your ability to make the most of strange and interesting opportunities as they arise. Career development professionals can help you develop and use the following resilient career skills:

- Curiosity
- Flexibility
- Risk-taking
- Optimism
- Cultural diversity

Curiosity

Curiosity is a skill you will need to be committed to for lifelong learning. Learning doesn't stop when you finish your degree. By cultivating curiosity, you will make the most of different opportunities, and you will be continuously learning. For example, a student who is interested in healthcare realizes his soccer coach is also a registered nurse. Following up on his curiosity, the student asks the coach if he could visit the hospital and shadow his work. The student finds it very helpful to discuss with him what it is like to be a male in a predominately female field. The student also meets a PCA at the hospital who encourages him to apply for part-time jobs. With a part-time job, the student can explore patient care and make a more informed decision about career choices. In this case, the student acted on his curiosity and learned about various opportunities that, as they unfolded, brought nursing to the forefront as a potential change of career direction for him.

I encourage you to follow curiosity and create deliberate opportunities to explore specific careers. Decision-making is a process of exploration and commitment. Career decisions are no different. Through traditional methods like navigating the Web, conducting informational interviews, shadowing, and pursuing internships, you can gather information to help yourself explore your curiosity and then make informed and responsible choices.

I want you to know that it is normal to experience distress during the exploration process. As you follow your curiosity and engage in the process, you may experience doubts, confusion, anxiety, and other forms of distress. But by taking charge of your career and taking an active role, you will build your resiliency and come to see doubts and anxiety as just part of the process. Taking an active role helps you cope, regulate your emotions, and think healthy thoughts. You are not a victim of decisions others make; you can transform your curiosity into opportunities for learning and exploration.

TIP

Reflect often on what motivates and drives you in life. More specifically, what drives your curiosity? Is there a specific challenge in society you would like to solve? Reflection fosters learning, new perspectives, and self-awareness. It motivates you to seek out knowledge, new experiences, and a willingness to embrace the uncertain and unpredictable.

Flexibility

To accept that change is a constant in life and that it will happen whether it is planned or not is a realistic and healthy way of thinking. Developing this perspective on change will challenge you to think creatively and flexibly about your future. To be flexible and resilient is to have the ability to shift perspectives and to think clearly and thoroughly while adapting to new realities. Embracing unusual solutions, encouraging outside-the-box viewpoints, and challenging previous belief systems are some of the ways to increase your adaptability skills.

For example, do you believe that to be happy you must have a rewarding career? Do you believe that one's worth as a person is strongly related to his/her occupational choice? What did you notice about these two questions? Did you realize they are both imperatives? These two statements assume that you have a precise, fixed idea of how a career should and/or must be. If you believe these statements, it is likely you will be stressed and place rigid demands on yourself.

It is important that you think flexibly and realize there are many other factors in your life that will play a role in determining your worth as a person.

Many students have changed majors because they are not progressing, others have postponed summer internships because of COVID-19, various others have learned to network in breakout rooms through Zoom, and several others have adapted to WFH (working from home), among other realities in which students needed to show flexibility to adapt and be resilient to new circumstances.

Career development professionals can assist you in clarifying your ideas and being less rigid in life by viewing difficulties as challenges instead of paralyzing events. You will need to distinguish when to be persistent, particularly when dealing with obstacles and barriers, and when to be flexible to adapt to a situation and change plans. To achieve your career goals, you will need to act with conviction, staying motivated and adaptable. When things don't go as planned, embrace your frustration and take it for what it is. You can see failures and mistakes as lessons to be learned from and opportunities for growth.

TIP

When applying for jobs, show potential employers different scenarios where you demonstrated persistence to continue achieving and flexibility to change course. Show them how your mind can focus on possibilities rather than deficiencies and what you have learned from failures. To show resiliency to an employer, be prepared to expand on a situation where you demonstrated flexibility. Likewise, be ready to support your statement with an experience that illustrates what you have learned from failure.

Risk-Taking

Risk-taking can be intentional. Intentional risk-taking is motivated by purpose. There is a relationship between risk-taking and opportunity. When your career goals are informed by your values, it is probable that you will take some chances in life to achieve your career outcomes.

Please answer this simple question: Do you like chocolates? Yes? No?

Now answer my follow-up question: How do you know if you like them or not?

The answer is because you have tried them, correct? Although not as simple, you'll never know what career outcome may come of a decision unless you try it.

Remaining curious and exploring your options can reduce the probability of having a different outcome than the one expected. You also need to know your actions or inactions may cause surprising and negative results.

This is when fear comes into play. Many people do not act on their choices because of fear of failure or, for some, fear of succeeding. Sometimes you may feel it is better to maintain the status quo than to admit that you are afraid of making a wrong decision.

But that's the power of decision-making. It can bring change to your life! It can teach you, as Dr. Susan Jeffers (2013) says, to feel your fear and do it anyway. Fear will not go away because you are deciding. Furthermore, have you realized that the more frightened you are, the closest you probably are to making a choice? As she mentioned, the only way to change, once and for all, is to act and surpass oneself. Acting is how we progress towards greater self-confidence and resilience. Resilience requires action. Action is a great restorer and builder of confidence.

Inaction is not only the result of fear but also its cause.

Ask Yourself: What stops you from being the person you want to be and live the life you dream of?

It is your responsibility to take risks and act on your curiosity by being persistent, a problem solver, and flexible with your choices. Only you can take decisive actions, knowing that chance and luck also have a say in everything that happens. Acting on your choices will demand being attentive to the opportunities that come to you and the ones you create for yourself.

TIP

Fear can hold you back from taking calculated risks that can lead to good outcomes. Think about what you could be losing when you do not take risks. It takes courage to leave your comfort zone and confront your fears. Instead of saying to yourself, "I can't because," wonder "How can I?" and be more conscious and purposeful about your decision-making and the ongoing process of career development.

Optimism

Optimism is a valuable trait to cultivate. Being optimistic brings a positive outlook to decision-making and joyful energy to career development. In the midst of many challenges, optimists see opportunities as opposed to difficulties. They tend to look for meaning in adversity, which makes them more resilient in life. Optimists are also very realistic. They have learned to balance hope with their trust of their assessment of the present moment. This results in them having confidence in their future and outcomes.

Career development professionals can assist you in cultivating optimism. They will help you learn how to turn criticism from others and self-criticism into constructive thoughts and actionable steps. Researchers have found that key personal attributes such as confidence, resilience, and optimism correlate with career clarity, job satisfaction, job fit, and alignment between job and career expectations. Optimists not only feel more hopeful but also score higher in career curiosity and exploration. Optimists talk about their strengths and blessings, which helps them keep a positive attitude in life.

An optimist is someone who can separate their identity and self-worth from their career choices. For instance, believing you are a loser because you did not get job offers after many interviews is a dangerous thought. It is untrue and creates unnecessary emotional turmoil. Be mindful that you are not your career; rather, you express yourself through one. For example, it is different to say "I am a counselor" than to say "I do counseling work" or "I play the role of a counselor." What would happen if you lose your job? Do you lose yourself or the image you have created of yourself? Remember, you are always more than your career, more than the job you hold.

TIP

Optimists strive to learn how to maintain a healthy work-life balance. Research shows many people who have successful long-term careers have learned to maintain higher energy levels, both at school and work. Ask yourself how you could bring more enthusiasm to your life. Is your life out of balance? Inquiring about an organization's best work-life balance practices is a good question for you to ask during an interview. The answer will show you a lot about the potential fit between you and the organization.

Diversity

For a diverse workforce to work effectively, the understanding of difference must be ingrained and valued in company culture. Diversity is a strength, allowing organizations and teams to adopt different lenses and approaches to solving challenges and operating the organization. A diverse team brings creativity and unique perspectives to problem-solving, working with customers and clients, and professional development of employees.

Conduct your research to assess diversity and your capacity to adapt and be resilient. Try to identify the numbers and promotion and retention practices of an organization related to how they seek to recruit/retain a diverse workforce. Get the inside scoop on the company's politics by employing the "six degrees of separation" strategy: See if you know someone who knows someone who works for the organization in question. Follow associated social media. If you are concerned, expand your research to include possible Equal Employment Opportunity lawsuits pending against the organization.

Find the organization's statements and activities to raise awareness of diversity issues and nondiscrimination policies (e.g., move in vs. move up). Look for what types of professional development and training opportunities they offer, what type of public support of diversity issues they demonstrate in the community, and what type of employee resource groups are available. You can use these recommendations to evaluate how diversity friendly a company may be and how resilient you will need to be to adapt to its culture.

A company that demonstrates commitment to diversity and inclusion should offer a work culture that favors flex time, mentoring programs, remote work, and flexible benefits. Unless workplaces can be spaces where people who share different backgrounds can enjoy the same right to work, then the employers themselves become just one more actor in the history of division and conflict.

> **TIP**
>
> Use your interviewing skills to ask about diversity. You can ask what is important to the organization and what is its work culture. For example, it is perfectly acceptable to ask about the roles diversity and inclusion play in their workplace. Pay attention if your questions are perceived as unwelcome. This will give you insight into how you might or might not fit within the company's culture. What questions related to diversity are important for you to ask?

Let's Review!

Career development is a process that demands that you be open-minded, that you embrace change, chance, and choice. It is a process that challenges you to be resilient and adaptable as well as curious and attentive to act on opportunities that present themselves to you. It encourages you to be flexible, to change course and be persistent when needed. Lastly, it urges you to take risks despite your fears and respond to the demands of a diverse workforce with an optimistic outlook in life. In short, career development demands resilience.

Ask Yourself: With all of these demands, how can you adapt to change and not be defeated by it?

You can practice resilience and career choice through purposeful and meaningful self-discovery. This way, you can make decisions that help you have more say in your path and place in society.

A Life of Meaning and Purpose

When have you felt most fully alive? As you think about your career path, finding meaningful work is an important component to consider. How does your choice of your major/career(s) respond to the needs of society? To your sense of personal fulfillment?

On one hand, your life of meaning and purpose will support what matters to you; on the other, it keeps you motivated in the face of adversities. You become highly resilient when you have the courage to experience your career failures as they come. This can be easier when you are doing work that matters to you. Take the time to learn about yourself when you experience a rejection or a loss. Notice your feelings and how they inform your thoughts and actions. You don't get stronger by staying in your comfort zone. You get stronger through the struggles. You can't make your feelings go away, but you can move through them and take action in healthy ways.

Career counselors can support you when you experience career losses, and they can help you stay grounded in what gives you meaning and purpose in your life. The artist Picasso wrote, "The meaning of life is to find your gifts. The purpose is to give them away." That's a beautiful way of describing a fulfilling life of work: as a gift that you give away.

As difficult as losses can be, they can also teach you to be intentional and deliberately grateful for your gifts. What makes you angry, frustrated, sad, frightened, indignant, and/or disappointed? What can you offer to make a difference? Sometimes your real gifts hide in these feelings, where meaning waits to be discovered.

Purpose often arises from curiosity about your own life, your feelings of frustration, the obstacles that you have encountered, and your resilience to overcome them. You know you are living a life with passion and purpose when you take risks to do something bold and in line with your core values and even when you are afraid about what might happen. Consciously shift your perspective by being grateful for your gifts, your talents, and the people around you. Be curious about what you might do with your gifts next.

Career development is a field that puts an emphasis on gratitude. It reminds us that it is always a good relationship practice to send thank-you notes. Thank-you notes for interviews are proper etiquette. They make your recipients feel valued and appreciated. Sending thank-you notes shows your ability to be attentive and respectful. Thank-you notes are also expected.

People notice if you send them. They also notice if you don't.

Gratitude is also at the heart of networking and the relationships you have established that are open to you. Be grateful to those who have mentored and given you advice, who have helped you throughout your career, and who have offered you an interview, a job, an opportunity. Regularly thank these people. Practicing gratitude can help you be happier overall, leading to genuine personal and professional relationships. Ultimately, more often than not, you will also learn to appreciate the difficulties in your life. These opportunities have taught you resiliency, leading you towards a gratitude for life itself, for what matters, and for what it has given you.

TIP

Look for opportunities for self-discovery and for identifying your gifts. Sometimes it is helpful to remember what you loved doing when you were 8 years old. Has this love persisted in your life? Your gifts will be something that you feel you are naturally good at and enjoy doing. They are something you care deeply about, and they fit your values. Purpose in life arises not only from your special gifts but also from your connections to others. Listen to what others appreciate about you. Think about how your strengths have made life better for others.

Career development professionals can assist you in deeply reflecting on your values and how they inform your life. Ask them to help you explore your values through a values card-sorting exercise. These cards will prompt you to consider a range of values (some that you may not have heard about) and to have a discussion about them and what they mean to your life, your career, and the society you live in.

Your Retirement Party

Now you are nearing the end of your career, and a small intimate party has been organized to celebrate your retirement. At this point, you are 65, and your colleagues and loved ones want to commemorate this important milestone. This party is all about celebrating your professional journey! Your partner has provided a blank memory book for your guests to write down their best memories of you and their greatest wishes for your future. Additionally, your partner has asked them to share with all guests stories about your achievements, your work history, and any anecdotes that are expressions of your character.

- What special memories would you like to hear?
- What unique contributions would they mention that are dear to your heart?
- What challenging situations would they cite that show your career resilience?
- What about your character? Any traits that you would like them to highlight?
- What messages for your future would you like to read in your memory book?
- Did your colleagues articulate well what you value most in life? What matters to you?

This has been an opportunity to reflect upon your career. Now is your time to express your gratitude to your colleagues and loved ones. What would you like to say to them before they leave your party?

Thoughts About What's Next

Fast changes in information and communication technology combined with current economic and political instability, a pandemic health crisis, and a more diverse and competitive global market have created a workforce that has caused involuntary job losses, lateral job movements, and career interruptions. In this world, where organizations seem to focus on the work and not necessarily the workers, employers will demand a resilient and competent workforce that can adapt to change, even when the circumstances seem discouraging and disruptive. Within this context, decision-making is necessary, hard, and compromised but also meaningful and essential, both for society and yourself.

To fulfill your sense of meaning and purpose, you need to become career resilient. You will need to be curious enough to ask questions, to explore and gather information; persistent and flexible enough to deal with career obstacles; willing to take risks that allow you to maximize the benefits from unplanned events; and optimistic enough to hold a positive attitude about your future.

In addition, you will need to be planful and utilize your resources, including those at your college or university, so you can be strategic about your career. Students who are resilient use information about themselves and situations and develop insightful, confident, and realistic career identities. By learning transferable skills, writing resumes and cover letters, interviewing, and creating your personal brand, you can focus on your strengths, your areas of growth, and your value for an organization. Through learning negotiation and networking skills, you can build and maintain professional relationships. Your interactions will teach you how to contribute, ask for assistance, and agree to disagree in the workplace and in your personal life.

Remember, career is an expression of your identity and life story. It is also your place in society where you can serve and impact. As you engage in your decision-making process about your career, practice your resilience-building skills. They will prepare you to push hard through difficult times and learn from yourself with dignity and intention.

References

Brooks, K. (2017). *You majored in what? Designing your path from college to career.* Plume.

Jeffers, S. J. (2013). *Feel the fear and do it anyway.* Vermilion.

CHAPTER 6

Spiritual Resilience

Mark Young, PhD & Lindsey Carelli, MA

Introduction

Wellness and Spirituality

Virtually every model of wellness includes the idea that spirituality is an essential element of a healthy life (Roach & Young, 2012). Wellness models imply that each of the dimensions affect the other components. This is the notion of "holism," which suggests that improvements in one arena can boost us in others. In the spiritual realm, for example, we know that people who meditate (spiritual) naturally improve their mental, emotional, and even physical health. Surprisingly, this solitary activity leads to better interpersonal relationships as well. Thus, spirituality gives us an invisible means of support.

What Is Spiritual Resilience?

Spiritual resilience is the ability to bounce back from stresses and challenging life events. Whether you were raised in a religious home, visited a church, mosque, or temple on major holidays, or had little exposure to such communities, becoming spiritually resilient can help you rebound during times of stress. One does not have to be religious to be spiritually resilient. Spiritual resilience is also important for atheists, who do not ascribe to a theistic view of the world, as well as agnostics, who cannot be certain that a divine power exists. Theism, or belief in God, is not required for one to engage in spiritual practices. They still have the power to uplift us in difficult times.

What Are Religion and Spirituality?

Although there are different ways of looking at it, the term "religion" usually means the organizations that people belong to, the rites and rituals they practice, and the associated beliefs they ascribe to as a group. At their best, religious and spiritual communities help us learn to direct our attention away from our self and refocus it on others in our community, nation, world, and/or the divine. They help us become compassionate through service. This refocusing on the needs of others takes place not at the expense of care for the self but out of an understanding of our interconnectedness.

Spirituality, on the other hand, is a characteristic of an individual. It is one's personal connection and experiences of a higher power. Spiritual experiences include feelings of love, happiness, serenity, and light. People usually have spiritual experiences when they are silent, in group prayer or meditation, and often when they are alone. Many famous spiritual seekers have these experiences in natural places, such as in deserts or caves, beside rivers, in mountains, or under trees. For most of us, periods of quiet are not routine and are difficult to find. We are bombarded with social media, phones, people talking, music in the car, and the sounds of traffic. Spiritual experiences seem to take place most often when we are very quiet. In the next section, we look at how to make oneself more available to spiritual experiences.

Cookbook for a Spiritual Life

Below are some ways to develop the spiritual aspect of your life. Just like any other dimension of wellness, to enhance spirituality, we must focus on it and practice it regularly. Here we will talk about prayer and meditation, locating meaning, becoming more empathic and compassionate, service to others, and finding a spiritual community.

Prayer and Meditation

Besides finding times to be quiet, the basic tools for a spiritual life are prayer and meditation. Depending on the religious tradition in which you were raised, you might be drawn to one more than the other. The commonality is that the mind is directed away from the world and focused on the inner life. Later we describe some ways to access these sources of inner strength.

Locating Meaning as a Path to Spirituality

This quote from Nietzsche says that if you have meaning and purpose in your life, you can endure the challenges, the roadblocks, and the empty feeling when life doesn't seem to make sense. Spirituality helps locate meaning and purpose in our lives, connecting us to something bigger than ourselves. Some

> He who has a why to live can bear almost any how.
>
> —Nietzsche

people refer to this "something bigger" as God. Others locate "something bigger" through personal accomplishments or dedication to their communities. These experiences of "something bigger" help us mature by moving us from self-centeredness and helping us develop the skills of compassion and empathy.

Why are we talking about a sense of meaning in a chapter on spiritual resilience? Having a higher purpose beyond our little self is always a spiritual endeavor. Whenever we focus on something beyond ourselves, that *is* a transcendent experience. It evokes strength, optimism, and other positive emotions. Positive emotions can combat negative ones like depression. We develop what Maddi (1998) called "existential courage." We are insulated from doubt and despair by our direction in life.

The Need to Belong as a Search for Meaning

One of the strongest needs for college students is the need to belong and form close relationships. Fraternities, sororities, clubs, and organizations were constructed to meet this basic human need. If you've taken Psychology 101, you know Maslow proposed that once we feel physically safe and secure, the need to have a tribe and develop intimate relationships is the next need that surfaces.

People find meaning by belonging to a group. Some groups are healthy and provide a sense of meaning and personal growth, and some are unhealthy and normalize destructive behavior. For example, the Impressionist painters formed a cohesive and supportive group that brought out the best in each painter and created a whole new school of art. On the other hand, some groups exploit their members and expect members to do things that go against their principles.

Student Organizations Can Help You Find Meaning

Getting involved with a student organization allows you to connect with like-minded peers and find your community on campus. Organizations offer regular opportunities to connect with others and the chance to widen your social circles outside your major and residence hall. Universities provide financial support for organizations, which means they have small budgets to host events and invite speakers. It is exciting to work alongside others to bring a speaker to campus to give a talk on a topic about which you are passionate. Along with cultivating professional development skills, this experience can also contribute to a sense of meaning. If your institution does not have the kind of organization you are seeking, research the process of starting a new organization.

Forgiveness and Spiritual Resilience

Forgiveness is giving up an expectation of justice that is making you suffer. It does not mean allowing someone to continue to take advantage of you, nor is it just a mental decision to forgive. It is a process that takes time and may not be achieved immediately following the event. Learning to forgive is a spiritual task because it means giving up your moral superiority and victimhood and focusing on the future rather than ruminating about the past. Many people believe that we can receive spiritual help through prayer and meditation to overcome our resentments. You may not be able to overcome your feelings of anger and hurt on your own, so you should consider seeing a counselor or therapist to help you in this process.

Service as a Path to Spirituality

Service is a natural outgrowth of compassion for others. But it also increases our compassion and helps us overcome stereotypes about others. It takes us out of ourselves and is therefore a spiritual endeavor. Listed below are some creative ideas about how to get involved with service in a small way. Many of these ideas can be aided by using an online signup application, such as SignUp.com or SignUpGenius.

Below are 10 ideas for service projects:

1. Organize tutoring for a class that many students find difficult. Partner with the professor and use online signup to match approved tutors with tutees.
2. Start an annual campus cleanup day when students volunteer to pick up trash.
3. Music students can offer free music workshops for elementary students in the community.
4. Ask the college's admissions office to partner with a local middle school allowing low-income students to follow college students for a day to class, in the dining hall, or to a sporting event.
5. Consider developing an after-school program for elementary students in which college students help them with their homework.
6. Ask your college bookstore to give away clearance clothing to homeless shelters.
7. Organize a group of friends to cook a meal at a local soup kitchen.
8. Volunteer at an assisted living facility, reading or playing games with residents.
9. Organize an art fair where students sell their pieces for dorm room art. Money raised can be donated to buy art supplies for a local school.
10. Ask a local yoga teacher to hold a class on campus and encourage participants to donate to assist community members in need.

Finding a Spiritual Community

How to know if a spiritual group is healthy. The term "cult" has no standard definition. It is frequently used to mean any religious organization that is outside the mainstream. As we look at history, that definition could easily apply to all the major religions in their early years. Instead, let's talk about healthy and unhealthy spirituality. To determine if a spiritual group is healthy or unhealthy, consider the following questions:

1. Is money a major focus of the group? Is the group open to those who can't pay?
2. Are there various levels you must aspire to that require increasing financial commitments?
3. Is the group honest about its purpose? For example, they say they are there to help the community but really focus on recruiting new members and never really give back.
4. Does the group promote fear of the outside world, focusing on enemies and rejection by nonmembers?
5. Does the group ask you to break ties with your religion, your friends, or your family?
6. Do they enforce their rules and eject those who don't follow them?
7. Does the group believe that they are right and every other spiritual path is wrong?
8. Can you leave the group without consequences or pressure?

As we look back on this list, these cautions seem a little scary, but there are also many spiritual groups that promote personal growth and transformation through prayer, service, meditation, and education. They don't require you to change your name, donate, change your clothing, or fast. Do your research.

Wellness and Resiliency Tips

Finding Meaning

1. Explore and Find a Vocation
   The term "vocation" comes from the same root as the word "vocal," and it means a calling. My job may be physician's assistant, but my calling is healing. How does one find a calling? I believe we stumble into it by going through various jobs and then realizing a common theme. For example, when I (Mark) look back at my earliest jobs (lifeguard, camp counselor, correctional counselor), I see a common element of helping. Maybe you haven't had enough experiences yet to see that theme. Consider volunteering. Every job, paid or not, helps you recognize what you are drawn to and what you want to avoid.

2. Have Quality Conversations
   Quality conversations are those that address the big questions in life: What is our purpose? Is there a higher power? What happens after death? You may think there are no answers to these questions, but pondering and discussing these questions with professors, fellow students, and clergy can help you explore your own beliefs.

3. Make a Bucket List
   A bucket list is an inventory of all the experiences you want to have before you die. If you have a fairly long list, see if you can identify some themes, such as exploration and travel, friendships, family, achieving some status, learning things, etc. These themes might provide insight into what you find meaningful.

4. Find Themes and Patterns in Your Past Experiences
   A bucket list is focused on the future, but the past can also yield some clues to what we care about and value. Look at your previous jobs, internships, organizational memberships, and leadership positions. Are there common elements? For example, do you seek out leadership because you want to make a positive change in a system?

5. Make a Mission Statement for Your Life
   Companies and organizations create mission statements to encourage employees or members to stay on track and to determine if the organizations are going in the right direction. Individuals can set mission statements for their lives. Here are some examples:
   "To make a difference in the world by helping individuals learn and grow."
   "To encourage myself to develop all the skills I can and to recognize my strengths."

6. Follow Your Bliss
   Joseph Campbell, author of *Hero with a Thousand Faces*, recommended following your bliss as a means of self-actualization. He meant pursuing those things that intrigue you. The emotion of interest/excitement is a positive emotion that opens us up and broadens our perspective. If we are excited about something, we encounter related ideas and find new avenues of inquiry. Following your interests increases curiosity and decreases self-doubt. One of the discoverers of the structure of the DNA molecule consistently tested in the average range of intelligence even though he had won a Nobel Prize. He often said he wasn't the smartest person in the world but he was more curious than anyone he had ever known. Many times, people don't follow their bliss and choose careers that seem practical or financially rewarding. Sometimes they are unhappy later in life. Although it sounds scary to rely on your sense of excitement and wonder, it is a way of arriving at a meaningful life. Campbell says, "Follow your bliss." Don't be afraid, and doors will open up for you.

Enhancing Spirituality

Below are four simple ways you can immediately begin to get in touch spiritually—ways that will help you appreciate religion and spirituality and use your own spiritual resources to recover from the stresses of life.

1. Spend time in nature.
   Besides the mental and emotional benefits of being in nature, it is a place to achieve quiet and experience the beauty of creation. Being in nature can help us gain perspective and help us get a feeling for our place in the universe.
2. Find a regular solitary exercise routine or take a hatha yoga class.
   Exercise can help us physically, but when done with attention, it keeps us inner focused rather than other focused.
3. Attend a service of a faith other than your own.
   The benefit of seeing how others practice is enlightening, like traveling to another country. It makes us recognize that there are many ways to worship, helps us get unstuck from our prejudices, and corrects misinformation.
4. Practice meditation/prayer daily.
   If practiced regularly, sitting in silence is the simplest and most effective way to have spiritual experiences. It takes very little time to get the benefit of reduced stress and helps us look at life from a new angle.

EXERCISES/TECHNIQUES

I. The Spiritual Journey

Gather a blank piece of paper, a pencil, and markers or colored pencils if you have them. As you reflect on the themes covered in this chapter, consider the events of your own life. What religious or spiritual milestones have you experienced? What communities have you been connected to? Which individuals have encouraged you to grow spiritually? Recall times when you have been able to offer forgiveness, experienced awe, or have been overwhelmed with gratitude. When did you face roadblocks in your spiritual journey? How did you overcome them? Arrange your responses to these prompts chronologically, and illustrate each of them. For some, this looks like a path up a mountain or through a forest, containing dead ends and forks in the road, with each milestone represented along the way. For others, a more abstract picture emerges, such as a maze or labyrinth. Don't feel constrained by these examples; allow yourself the space of creative expression.

  After you create an image of your journey, step back and look at the big picture. Take in the highs and lows that brought you to where you are right now. Consider the paths you want to continue traveling as well as the crossroads you would like to leave behind. Which ingredients from the cookbook or tips listed above might aid you in those goals? Create a plan to integrate them into your routine.

II. Silent Meditation 101

SOS meditation (Singh, 2013) is a simple but effective method of meditation that has been shown to decrease stress and increase empathy in students (Gutierrez, Conley, & Young, 2016). Practiced daily, meditation has been found to help your physical, mental, emotional, and spiritual well-being. Begin with as little as 5 or 10 minutes and slowly build up to 20 or 30 minutes per day. Research shows regularity is crucial to getting the stress-reduction benefits.
Instructions:

- Sit comfortably in any pose in which you can remain for an extended period.
- Close your eyes gently, just as you do when you go to sleep, but remain wide awake.

- Focus your attention 8–10 inches in front of you.
- Mentally repeat any calming word or phrase slowly, at an even pace. This silent repetition prevents the mind from wandering.
- You may see flashes of light, circles of light, or lights of various colors. When your attention is focused, you see the light.
- Keep your attention focused in the middle of the experience and enjoy its calming and peaceful effect.

III. Loving Kindness Meditation

1. Sit in a comfortable position, as you would for meditation.

2. Gently close your eyes and allow the breath to continue at its normal pace.

3. Gather your attention at your heart. Cultivate a sense of loving presence as you repeat the following phrases slowly and silently, directing your attention in the following ways:

   a. Begin with yourself.

      May I be happy. May I be healthy. May I be at peace.

   b. Now, think of a loved one. This can be a romantic partner, a close friend, a sibling, or a family member. While many people may come to mind, choose one person to focus on.

      May they be happy. May they be healthy. May they be at peace.

   c. Next, think of someone you do not know. Perhaps it is someone you have seen around campus but have never spoken to. Recall their face in your mind.

      May they be happy. May they be healthy. May they be at peace.

   d. Then think of all the people who make up your campus community—all the students, faculty, staff members, and alumni who are part of this network. Direct your loving awareness to them.

      May they be happy. May they be healthy. May they be at peace.

   e. Finally, think of the world. Recall all the countries, people, animals, and beautiful natural wonders that you know. Send as much loving awareness as you can into the world.

      May we be happy. May we be healthy. May we be at peace.

Reflection Questions

1. **Belonging**

   None of us choose the identities we were born into—our race, ethnicity, or social class—and this is also true of our religious identity. Some people feel a sense of compatibility and satisfaction with the religious traditions of their families, while others do not. Many people are now growing up with no connection to a religious denomination. Cultivating spiritual resilience means establishing a sense of ownership in your involvement with a religious or spiritual community. Write down the qualities of the kind of community you are seeking. Why are these qualities important to you?

2. **Compassion**

   In her public talks, the religious writer Karen Armstrong says that compassion is "dethroning ourselves from the center of our world and putting another person there." Can you think of a time when you were able to show compassion to someone and you were able to take yourself completely out of the equation? How good are you at showing compassion for yourself? For example, are you able to forgive your mistakes as easily as you forgive those of others?

3. **Religious or Spiritual?**

   About 71% of U.S. adults call themselves Christians, with about 6% adhering to non-Christian faiths. Almost 23% are "none," adhering to no religion at all. The "nones" appear to be increasing. At the same time, about 70% of us call ourselves spiritual. Do you think people can be spiritual but not religious or religious and not spiritual?

4. **Forgiveness**

   Recall an event when you did not forgive someone for their injustice to you. If you gave up your need for justice and overcame your resentment, what would you be losing? Do you agree that forgiveness is a valuable way to develop spiritual resilience?

References

Gutierrez, D., Conley, A., & Young, M. E. (2016). Examining the effects of Jyoti meditation on stress and the moderating role of emotional intelligence. *Counselor Education & Supervision, 55*, 109–122.

Roach, L. F., & Young, M. E. (2012). Spirituality: Benefits of belief. In P. F. Granello (Ed.), *Wellness counseling* (pp. 157–174). Prentice Hall.

Singh, R. (2012). *Meditation as medication.* Radiance Press.

Worthington, E. L., Jr., Griffin, B. J., Toussaint, L. L., Nonterah, C. W., Utsey, S. O., & Garthe, R. C. (2016). Forgiveness as a catalyst for psychological, physical, and spiritual resilience in disasters and crises. *Journal of Psychology and Theology, 44*(2), 152–165.

CHAPTER 7

Your Corner of the World

Environmental Wellness

Matthew S. Fleming, MS, MA, LPCC-S

An ancient pond.
O! a frog jumps in—
a splash ...

—Basho, *Frog Poem*

Copyright © by Matsuo Bashō; trans. Alexander Sitnitsky (CC BY-SA 3.0) at https://en.wikisource.org/wiki/Translation:Frog_Poem_(Sitnitsky).

Image 7.1

Introduction

So far, this book has focused on internal and psychological aspects of resilience. This chapter is quite different in that it focuses on your external environment. Often we don't stop to consider how what goes on around us has such an impact on our lives. As you read this chapter, look to aspects of your life that you might be able to influence. As you become more active in addressing the environment around you, you can reclaim your power in your life. This chapter has a practical take on tips to help your environment. Feel free to pick and choose what is right for you, as not all of these suggestions will be appropriate for every student.

Your environment consists of all the things surrounding you. As you interact with your environment, you influence your environment, and your environment influences you. Some aspects of our environment are beyond our personal control. For example, you cannot choose your parents, the home you lived in when you were 5 years old, or which elementary school you attended. Some studies suggest that poverty/homelessness may contribute to as much as a 15-point difference in a person's IQ (Spence et al., 2004; Walton, 2018). These studies point out how those in poverty suffer from cognitive deficits. The studies are not conclusive about cause and effect (correlation vs. causation), but consider this: imagine how you would feel if you had to go without sleep for one night. Now extrapolate that to how you would feel if you had to sleep on the ground in a major city night after night. Do you think you would be able to engage in the more intricate aspects of your studies? Probably not. Many difficult childhood experiences can be addressed and recovered from, but some, like lead in the water supply in Flint, Michigan, are much harder to remediate.

Some components of your environment include safety, shelter, food, social interaction/support, exercise/physical activity, emotional tenor, and being with nature. As a new college student, you may have the ability to control more aspects of your environment than you could at home, but you still have to contend with financial concerns, roommates, and other challenges. It is challenging for many students to focus on wellness in their environment. There are many things you can do to improve your surroundings, and as you improve your environment, you may find that you are more successful in your studies and in your life.

The focus of this chapter is to examine aspects of one's environment that may hurt performance and to identify opportunities to improve your environment in ways that may be helpful. Some opportunities may require a level of discipline to implement, and some may impact your social life as you exercise better boundaries with the people around you. However, the potential payoff is a more successful college experience, and developing discipline is a skill that will support you beyond college.

Aspects of Your Environment You Can Address

Maslow presented a hierarchy of needs. At the bottom of the pyramid, Maslow suggests basic needs such as food and shelter must be met before we are able to take advantage of self-actualization and learning. Although we usually assume college students have these needs met, sadly, it is not uncommon to hear of college students who are sleeping in their cars for lack of shelter or trying to live on one package of ramen noodles a day. Aspects of these needs will be discussed in subsequent sections of this chapter.

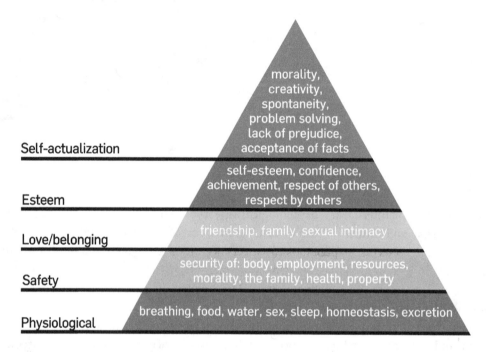

FIGURE 7.1   Maslow's Hierarchy of Needs

Safety

Safety is a key aspect of your well-being. If you are in an unsafe environment, you will spend a lot of energy scanning for potential threats that may harm you. Appeasing the need for safety promotes a more relaxed state and is more conducive to learning/study activities.

Safety starts with selection of a place to live while on campus. The maxim "location, location, location" is apropos. Oftentimes, universities are not located in the safest parts of town. If you're not living in the dormitory, seriously consider where you will be sleeping and how you will be getting to and from classes. This may entail trade-offs, such as renting a house in a less expensive part of town with your friends only to find out later that the area is a target for burglars or that you have to walk through an unsafe area to get to and from class, especially after dark. An area that looks peaceful during the daytime might feel different after dark if you hear sirens or gunshots. Check with your college for suggestions for safer places to live. In addition, it may be worth calling the police for feedback about the safety of an area you are considering living in.

Safety also pertains to making good choices about where to spend time with friends. A healthy choice might be to attend a movie or work out at the gym. Recognize that it is risky to socialize at a bar and to potentially overindulge in alcohol or other substances. Alcohol is the most prevalent date rape drug (sometimes made worse with the addition of substances like roofies). Alcohol is too often implicated in the times leading up to sexual assaults. This is not a PSA saying "Do not drink," but it is encouraging you to think about where to imbibe and how much alcohol to consume.

Sleep Hygiene

Once a safe living space has been secured, focus shifts to aspects of getting a good night's sleep. This is often referred to as "sleep hygiene."

How your bedroom is set up influences sleep quality and how alert you will feel the next day. There is a Zen saying: "Clean your room, clean your mind." Keep in mind that if your room is a chaotic mess, you will take on some of that chaos when you enter that space. Consider taking 5–10 minutes each day to tidy up your room, as that will contribute to better sleep and increased focus when you're awake.

Your room should be cool (not cold), quiet, and dark. If your room is too warm, consider opening a window if you are in a place where it is safe to do so, or use a fan. If your room is too cold, consider getting a small heater, providing it is safe and your apartment or dorm wiring can deal with the heater's current draw.

Darkness contributes to better sleep. Try to extinguish all light in your bedroom. If windows let in a lot of light, consider getting blackout drapes to block light from that window. If you share a room and your roommate keeps the lights on later than you want, try a sleep mask to block light from your eyes.

It is helpful to maintain a regular sleep schedule. As best you can, follow a relaxing pre-bedtime routine to calm your body and ease into a good night's sleep. Alcohol and stimulants interfere with sleep. Avoid caffeinated beverages after noon. If you consume alcohol, do so in moderation and, ideally, allow your body a couple of hours to clear out the alcohol before going to bed. Do not use alcohol as a sleep aid. It disrupts your sleep rhythms, and you will not wake up feeling well.

It is generally a good idea to turn off your electronics 60–90 minutes prior to sleep, as the light from those devices activates your nervous system and interferes with sleep. Smartphones are a major contributor to poor sleep, with their seemingly incessant beeping or vibrating. Consider turning off your phone at night (gasp!) or putting it in airplane mode so Internet and data notifications are blocked. The majority of students feel the need to check their phones whenever messages come in and then wonder why they can't get a good night's rest. If you are worried about missing an important call, consider installing a phone filter app that will only ring for numbers you specify, and you will also need to turn off the data portion of the phone to block Internet notifications. In addition, several research papers suggest that radio frequency energy emitted by phones may impact health, so consider using speakerphone when possible and not holding the phone next to your head (Višnjić et al., 2018; Van den Bulck, 2007).

Read a nondramatic book or magazine, meditate, relax, and maybe take a bath or shower. This might also be a good time to try some journaling. Make your bedtime routine one that supports your ability to relax and prepare for a good night's sleep.

Sleep occurs in cycles of deeper and shallower sleep. Many people, especially when anxious, will worry "I'm not sleeping" and then check the clock. Often, these people were sleeping lightly and woke themselves out of a shallow sleep cycle to check the clock. This trains one to wake up after each sleep cycle and perhaps have difficulty falling back to sleep. It does not matter what time you may have awakened; just relax with some deep breathing and ignore the clock. If your alarm clock has a glowing face, consider turning its face away from you so you cannot see it. If you don't sleep as well for one night, it will not impact your performance the next day too much, so don't worry.

Boundaries With Roommates

If you have roommates, consider having periodic discussions about boundaries. Kitchen and common areas can be the source of friction, as roommates may not respect what you feel is "yours." Disagreements left unaddressed fuel resentment or other forms of passive/aggressive responses. Typical areas that need to be addressed in shared living situations include 1) quiet hours, 2) chores, 3) bill paying and who contributes, and 4) food. Making these agreements explicit can head off many disagreements.

Defining quiet hours makes it less likely that you will be subjected to loud music all night long if one of your room-mates is a night owl. Quiet hours also foster downtime for your pre-bedtime routine, study, or other activities best done in quiet. Allow some room for exceptions that can be addressed by all roommates. For example, there might be an agreement to bend the rules for special occasions like that big party or football celebration.

A chore list can head off the tendency to say "Well, it's their job, so I will just ignore the mess." Your parents are not present to help with this (unless you are living at home), so having a discussion about expectations for how often to clean, what to clean, and who is responsible go a long way toward ensuring harmony. Expectations for cleanliness will vary from person to person, so try to maintain a flexible attitude and be willing to compromise. It is often useful to place the chore list in a conspicuous place where all residents can see it.

Discussions about food are important to delineate what food is for common use and what food is "yours." It may be helpful to designate a space for each person's private food stash and a place for food that is available to all. Consider if you want to cook meals and possibly eat together. If sharing cooking responsibilities, schedule in advance to avoid confusion. This can be part of the chore list as well.

If you and your roommates share expenses, it is helpful to discuss who pays, how much, and when. Set up a bill-paying schedule so everyone knows the expectations of when the rent, utilities, and cable bill are paid. Make sure you include who pays for the use of "premium" entertainment options that might incur extra charges.

Food

When you reach for any food, first pause and ask yourself "Why am I eating this food?" If you are truly hungry, then eating is a good remedy. Often, however, we feel some general unpleasant feeling, label that as "hungry," and eat when we are not actually hungry. Eating is not an optimal solution for feelings like boredom, stress, effect (eating to feel a certain way), filling a void (emotional), or loneliness. If you can identify a need other than being truly hungry, it is possible to select a more satisfying and appropriate course of action. For example, if you are lonely, call a friend. If you are bored, take a break to participate in some uplifting activity.

What you eat has a significant impact on how you feel, think, and perform. Food is an important energy and nutri-tion source. Without energy, you cannot function well, and without a good balance of calories and nutrition, organ or tissue systems in your body may fail.

Generally, it is better to eat foods that are less processed, as processing often depletes nutrients from otherwise nutritious foods. Many processed foods are designed to be addictive and have hidden sugars and fats so there is a tendency to overeat. "Empty calories" refers to foods that provide high calorie levels but low nutrition levels. Exam-ples of empty calories might include fast food, candy, salty snacks such as Doritos, beer, and fancy coffee with whips, syrups, or sprinkles.

There are too many dietary regimens to list. We show one example to highlight the difference between the tradi-tional food pyramid (eight servings of grain each day) with another alternative. This is not an endorsement of this diet, as your health makeup will dictate a lot about the best diet for you (see your doctor). The popular Mediterranean diet, inspired by the eating habits of people in Spain, Italy, and Greece, emphasizes eating vegetables, whole grains, olive oil, and fish and consuming red meat only occasionally. The Mediterranean diet is rich in nutrients from foods that are lower on the glycemic index (Foster-Powell et al., 2002). Conversely, foods high on the glycemic index, such as cereal or a baked potato, are very rapidly converted into sugars in your body, setting up a situation where the body overcompensates by producing insulin and then crashing when blood sugar drops. Experiencing a crash can leave you feeling hungry again in short order, stimulating overeating. Over time, eating too many high-carbohydrate, starchy foods may contribute to weight gain, heartburn/acid reflux, type 2 diabetes, depression, and other ailments. Consult with a doctor or nutritionist before making any significant changes in your diet so they can review your specific health profile. Often these resources can be accessed on campus at the student health center or counseling center for free or minimal charge.

FIGURE 7.2 Mediterranean Diet

Social

Human beings are the most social animals on the planet. Lacking social contact leads to many mental and physical health issues. There is good reason that in prison, solitary confinement is felt to be the worst thing an inmate might have to endure. Many find even 24 hours of forced solitude to be too much to bear.

This book is being written during the peak of the COVID-19 pandemic, which is a new novel virus humans have no inherent immunity to and is very contagious. During the pandemic, most social contact needs to shift to virtual, both for social interaction and for learning. This is less than ideal, but there is hope that an effective vaccine may be available in 2021 so the COVID constraint on social gatherings may be relieved. Using virtual connections via Zoom or other software takes a little more effort, but many are finding applications to chat, play games, and learn that connect them with others.

Image 7.2

Affiliation

As you begin your college experience, try to identify venues where you can engage with people and activities that lift your spirits. No one finds connections with everyone, and you will find yourself feeling either uplifted or drained and used as you engage with others. Pay attention to how you feel during and after an encounter. If you feel uplifted and positive about yourself, then the relationship is probably worth putting in the effort to cultivate. On the other hand, if you feel drained or somehow used, evaluate whether the relationship is necessary (you may not like a professor, but if they are teaching a course required for graduation, you may have to put up with it), and if it is not, maybe withdraw from that relationship.

Look for study buddies in your classes. Your mutual desire to learn the course material is a good opportunity to meet others and learn more about them as you work on the course materials together. Sometimes this is the start of a wonderful friendship.

Many students find it worthwhile to explore some of the university's numerous student organizations and clubs for fellowship with others who share similar interests and networking for professional growth. At The Ohio State University (2021), there are over 1,400 student organizations, including diverse options such as volunteering, dance,

GLBTQI, grilling (yes, they get together to cook), rock climbing, and many, many more. In addition, universities may also support a student starting their own student organization with a minimum of five other students. OSU even provides nominal financial support for their student start-up organizations. Getting together with a "club" for a weekly game night may be a welcome outlet to relax and be social.

If you follow a particular faith tradition, it may be helpful to find a congregation in that tradition near your university. You may find inspiration from a sermon and be energized by fellowship. If you have questions about your faith, this may also be a time to explore other traditions to see where you find your best fit, including nondoctrinal congregations, such as humanists, the Universalists, and the United Church of Christ, which emphasize connection through how we treat our fellow humans. Other possibilities include Zen Buddhism, which does not address the existence of "God" one way or the other.

Dating

Many students continue to carry on with high school dating experiences, and others may start dating for the first time during college. This may be an exciting time for many and can be traumatic for some. Benefits of dating include getting to know someone very well, learning about yourself in relationships, and possibly finding the love of your life. The risks are that you might be hurt, manipulated, or otherwise let down.

Almost all of us have been emotionally wounded in some fashion. Do you know anyone who had a "perfect" childhood? If you experience repeated relationship failures, consider a few sessions with a counselor at your university's counseling center (often free of charge) to talk about what is happening in your relationships and seek insights as to how you possibly may be contributing to those failures. Reading psychologically oriented materials might also help you to know yourself better in a relationship. One example is *Bad Boyfriends* by Jeb Kinnison (2014). Kinnison talks about attachment theory in a way that may help you identify your attachment style and how to avoid those whose styles might be in conflict with yours.

Your dating experience will go better if you realize that you are perfect as you are. Wait, perfect? Yes, you are. Never let someone tell you that you should give up on your principles in order to please them. You are not looking for a relationship to fix or complete you, and you will always be disappointed if you do. So look for someone who accepts you for who you are and honors what you value. This does not mean that you cannot learn about yourself from relationships and choose some different behaviors. An example of this is found in Temple Grandin's book *Thinking in Pictures* (Grandin & Sacks, 2006). Grandin has a condition called autism, which is a developmental disability that significantly affects verbal and nonverbal communication and social interaction. She did not easily pick up on social norms, and one of her friends suggested she was "stinky." This allowed Grandin to consider using deodorant to reduce her odor. It is important to note it did not change who she was or compromise her values. It is important that you not try to change your basic nature. As a therapist, I've seen too many long-term relationships end because one partner tried to make themselves what they perceived their partner wanted. This fuels resentment (often not even noticed by the person making the change) that causes the person to step back from the relationship and possibly to leave the relationship.

Your dating will be more successful if you can be clear about your own personal boundaries. Boundaries determine how close someone can come and what he/she can do to or with you. Examples of boundaries include things like:

- Who pays for the date or other entertainment?

- Do I drink alcohol or use substances? If so, how much will I use without compromising my ability to say "no" to things I do not desire?

- Do I have sex in a relationship? When? First date, fifth date, or wait for marriage? This does not imply what you should do but rather encourages you to know yourself and ask yourself what fits your values.

When dating, do you most desire intimacy or excitement? Hooking up generates a lot of excitement, but you may not really know the other person. So you get a release, but you may not see that person again. Conversely, learning more about a person over time lends itself to more intimacy in the relationship and has the potential to evolve sex into an intimate act with your partner as you explore each other's likes and dislikes. This distinction is important, as excitement will fade over time and lead to the desire to find a more exciting partner. However, if intimacy is cultivated, there is an opportunity to build that loving connection even stronger over time.

Exercise

There is a folk saying: "Tired body, exercise the mind. Tired mind, exercise the body." The college environment emphasizes the mind, often with less regard for your body. At one time or another, most students will hit a "wall" where it becomes hard to read their assignments and retain the information. When encountering that state of mind, reflect on whether or not you are getting enough exercise. This does not refer to how your body looks but rather suggests that moderate exercise can help you be happier and perform better academically. One of the positive benefits of exercise is that it produces chemicals in the body called endorphins, which trigger positive feelings and reduce your perception of pain.

Disclaimer: If you are considering significantly ramping up your exercise intensity, consult with a doctor about your health profile before starting the program to ensure you are ready to exercise safely.

Measuring steps and the Fitbit have become popular. Generally, users are encouraged to walk 7,000 steps (usually about 3 miles) each day to be fit. Walking is great, inexpensive exercise, and most healthy students can do it without investing in special equipment. Your university's fitness facilities offer classes that help jump-start an exercise habit.

Monitoring your heart rate can be a good gauge of whether you are working out at the right intensity (can be a brisk walk or hitting the weights). If you are not very fit, you may not have to work very hard to get your heart rate to the target mark. Conversely, as you become more fit, you will have to work harder to raise your heart rate. Many think that 40 minutes of exercise at 80% max heart rate is a good place to start. The American Heart Association (2021) lists maximum heart rates for different age groups and suggests that your max rate is 220 minus your age. If targeting 80% of max heart rate, multiply your max heart rate by 0.8.

Some research suggests that exercise that is cognitively challenging may have additional benefits over workouts that do not engage you cognitively (Raichlen & Alexander, 2020). This might suggest that sports requiring a lot of thinking, such as running plays in basketball or football, may strengthen your brain. Having said that, any exercise is better than no exercise.

Nature

Look at a flower or tree and pause. As you take in the flower, notice what happens in your body and how you feel. Get curious about what you see in the flower. Notice structures that may be present in other plants or even animals. Breathe. Let the flower fill the entirety of your attention. You stop time while attending to a natural object in this manner as you are one with the flower you are viewing. This act of being one with the flower is a powerful mindful exercise, and you will automatically relax as troubles and worries are suspended for a few moments.

We exist in nature and are dependent on nature for food, air, water, and shelter. We also exist in a fast-paced society that is largely split off from nature, so we don't notice the relationship between ourselves and nature. When we view nature (or any being) in this fashion, we convert them into an inanimate object to be used for our needs without much regard for the object as a living entity. In Genesis 1:26, God said man has dominion over the animals. If we see those animals as simply inanimate objects, then we should not be concerned if the animals we eat are raised in horrid conditions, as they are inanimate "things."

If nature is a thing to be used/consumed, we are left with a dilemma. What happens when we use up all of nature? In a word, we are in major trouble. With global warming upon us, we can see the impact of burning too much fossil fuel as glaciers melt, sea levels rise, and weather patterns become more intense and dramatic. Ultimately, the planet will be left with too little arable land and mass starvation, disease, and pestilence.

Our relationship with nature changes when we realize that we are part of nature rather than being separated from it. We can shift from being mindless consumers of nature to being stewards of nature. As stewards, we have a responsibility to care for the planet, just as a mother cares for her child. We start to see all plants and animals as miraculous creations to be cherished and used most carefully. As we more fully experience nature as a participator, we feel gratitude for each flower, each bee, and each tree. That gratitude enriches us and gives life meaning.

Stewardship can take the form of small actions or larger organized actions. Small actions include making food purchasing choices that have more environmentally friendly packaging, walking the two blocks to the library rather than driving, or picking up that candy wrapper you see discarded on the sidewalk. There are many organized opportunities to care for our planet, such as community-based forestry programs, and in urban areas, there are opportunities such as community gardening, tree planting, stream monitoring, reintroduction of endangered species, removal of invasive plants, etc. (Bennett et al., 2018).

Image 7.3

Taking time to be in nature may have psychological and physiological benefits for each of us. Sylvotherapy, also referred to as forest bathing (Shinrin-yoku) has been popular in Japan for years and is starting to become more widespread in the West. Forest bathing involves taking time to leisurely walk in the woods with no goal, simply strolling at an easy pace and allowing yourself to experience the trees, flowers, and birds. For the best effect, participants leave all cell phones and other distractions behind while in the woods.

Mathias et al. (2020) suggest several ways forest bathing (Shinrin-yoku) may benefit those who spend time among the trees. When in the forest, one is usually taken away, at least somewhat, from the urban environment, which often contains toxic volatile organic compounds (VOCs) released into the air as well as mold. Viewing the forest in a non-goal-oriented fashion, the natural sounds are soothing, and the smells of the forest are similar to essential oils that have been shown to improve relaxation. Physiological effects suggested are improvements to the immune system (Li, 2010), and decreased levels of stress hormones. Finally, Mathias suggests forest bathing can decrease stress, reduce aggressiveness, and improve mood.

Forest bathing does not have to cost you any money. Even if you are in a large city, parks are usually nearby where you can immerse yourself for an hour or two in nature. Even in one of the largest cities, New York City, Central Park affords plenty of space to get away for a while. Invite a couple of friends, leave your phones behind, and quietly amble through the woods. If you want a more in-depth experience, consider activities such as joining a hiking club or check your university's recreation pages to see if they offer student backpacking trips. Although not technically Shinrin-yoku, consider joining a birding club to explore nature and searching for birds.

Please consider that the planet takes care of us and it is up to us to care for the planet. If we are responsible stewards in how we use/interact with nature, we can have a happier life now and leave a better world for future generations.

EXERCISES

Here are a few things to try now:

- Turn off your phone at night. If you use it as an alarm clock, put your phone in airplane mode instead. Do this for 1 week. Notice if sleep improves.

- Block off a 2-hour space to walk in the woods. Any green space with trees will do, so use a nearby city park if larger forested areas are too far away. Take it slowly and allow yourself to be totally absorbed among the trees, flowers, and birds.

- Take an hour to take a brisk walk in the morning or afternoon. Try to get your heart rate up around 80% of your max heart rate. Notice if concentration for your studies is better afterwards.

Summary

We are products of our environment and are shaped by the world that surrounds us. Some things are difficult or beyond our control to change. For example, you cannot pick your parents, where you lived while growing up, or tomorrow's weather. Sometimes it feels like we cannot control much, and that may lead to feelings of powerlessness.

We can reclaim our power as we become active in addressing our surroundings to allow us to be more comfortable and effective within them. This is not always easy. As children, we are often told what to do, and we may carry that lack of power into adulthood. As an adult on your own, no one will tell you what to eat, when and how much to sleep, or who to affiliate with. The newfound freedoms of college can be exciting, but when we really consider it, we can be daunted by all the new responsibilities.

We are all part of the environment of others. "Others" include our friends, the trees and birds, and the planet at large. Realizing this, consider treating the whole world with kindness and care. We all share in our lives together, and living with love and kindness can make our lives better and allow us to make loving and appropriate decisions about ourselves and our lives.

It is understandable to worry that all of this is too much to take on. Start with baby steps in taking control of your relationship with your environment. Do not sell your power short. Look to role models like Malala Yousafzai, who is working for the education of Afghan girls, or Greta Thunberg, who is leading the charge to address global warming. Greta Thunberg started her movement with a school protest. These two young women risked a lot to champion the causes they chose. You can, too. Just do good in this world and take satisfaction in doing your best.

Reflection Questions

Consider the following points and reflect on what happens to you when you consider them:

1. Do you think you are part of your environment or separate from it? Think about how your response influences choices in your life.
2. The Bible suggests that man has dominion over the animals and the rest of the world. What responsibility do you take (or not) to be a steward for the animals and the world?
3. After reading this chapter, what changes will you try in your life?
4. Reread the quote from Basho at the beginning of this chapter. Imagine being that frog and reflect on what type of splash you want to make in your life and in the world.

References

American Heart Association. (2021). *Target heart rates chart.* https://www.heart.org/en/healthy-living/fitness/fitness-basics/target-heart-rates

Basho. (2003). *Frog poem.* Wikisource. https://en.wikisource.org/wiki/Translation:Frog_Poem_(Sitnitsky)

Bennett, N. J., Whitty, T. S., Finkbeiner, E., Pittman, J., Bassett, H., Gelcich, S., & Allison, E. H. (2018). Environmental stewardship: A conceptual review and analytical framework. *Environmental Management, 61*(4), 597–614. https://doi.org/10.1007/s00267-017-0993-2

Foster-Powell, K., Holt, S. H., & Brand-Miller, J. C. (2002). International table of glycemic index and glycemic load values: 2002. *The American Journal of Clinical Nutrition, 76*(1), 5–56. https://doi.org/10.1093/ajcn/76.1.5

Grandin, T., & Sacks, O. (2006). *Thinking in pictures: And other reports from my life with autism.* (2nd edition). Vintage Books.

Kinnison, J. (2014). *Bad boyfriends.* Author.

Li, Q. (2010). Effect of forest bathing trips on human immune function. *Environmental Health and Preventive Medicine, 15*(1), 9–17. https://doi.org/10.1007/s12199-008-0068-3

Mathias, S., Daigle, P., Dancause, K. N., & Gadais, T. (2020). Forest bathing: A narrative review of the effects on health for outdoor and environmental education use in Canada. *Journal of Outdoor and Environmental Education, 23*(3), 309–321. https://doi.org/10.1007/s42322-020-00058-3

Raichlen, D., Alexander, G.E. (2020, January). Why your brain needs exercise: Key transitions in the evolutionary history may have linked body and mind in ways that we can exploit to slow brain again. *Scientific American, 27–31.* http://scientificamerican.eoncontent.ebscohost.com/2328991

Spence, S., Stevens, R., & Parks, R. (2004). Cognitive dysfunction in homeless adults: A systematic review. *Journal of the Royal Society of Medicine, 97*(8), 375–379.

The Ohio State University. (2021). *Student organizations home: Student activities.* https://activities.osu.edu/involvement/student_organizations/

Van den Bulck, J. (2007). Adolescent use of mobile phones for calling and for sending text messages after lights out: Results from a prospective cohort study with a one-year follow-up. *Sleep, 30*(9), 1220–1223.

Višnjić, A., Veličković, V., Sokolović, D., Stanković, M., Mijatović, K., Stojanović, M., Milošević, Z., & Radulović, O. (2018). Relationship between the manner of mobile phone use and depression, anxiety, and stress in university students. *International Journal of Environmental Research and Public Health, 15*(4), . https://doi.org/10.3390/ijerph15040697

Walton, A. G. *How poverty changes your mind-set.* (2018). Chicago Booth Review. https://review.chicagobooth.edu/behavioral-science/2018/article/how-poverty-changes-your-mind-set

Credits

CHAPTER 8

Physical Resilience

Timothy R. Graham, MA, LPC, CHWC

[Sustainable systems + optimal stress] = *f* The core of physical resilience.

Have you ever thought about what age you will live to? Possibly not, as we do not have control over our destinies. Or do we? Have you ever thought about what the quality of life is that you want to have until your death—how good you physically feel and how well you can overcome the physical challenges you encounter throughout your lifespan? You *can* have control over this. But to do so, you must learn to adapt to the challenges you face through practice. These practices are the "medicines" that can help you achieve physical resilience. And the good news is that resilience can be learned.

Adversity can be considered one of the most powerful forces we encounter in life, especially one that can bring out our best or worst and anything else in between. The truth is, adversity does not discriminate, as everyone experiences this force at multiple points during their lifetime, and they experience it in different ways relative to their response. Adversity is not a one-size-fits-all punch. Life is unpredictable and messy, and bad things happen. However, we have a choice in how we respond to the adversity, and that is part of the human contract. When faced with adversity, how will you respond?

In this chapter, you will learn how both sustainable habits and regulating stress together make up the core of physical resilience. You will look at a conceptual model of physical resilience to understand how natural stressors produce functional recovery. You will learn strategies for how you can optimize stress in a healthy way through behavior change. It should become apparent through these concepts that you are in control of your systems, and the more intentional you are in the process, the greater your resilience will become when faced with adversity.

Optimal Stress

When an individual encounters an obstacle in life, such as stress, it can be characterized by four criteria (see Table 8.1); cumulation (magnitude of the stressor), predictability (timing of occurrence), duration (how long it lasts), and quality (stress that is beneficial versus bad for us). You may be surprised that stress is required to improve your physical resilience, as adaption only occurs when encountering an optimal stress load. Physical resilience benefits most from predictable, microcumulative, and situational stress encountered in our average day. The daily situational stress you encounter is similar to conditioning and preparing your body for when you encounter larger physical stressors. For example, situational adversity can be illustrated by exhibiting short-term stamina when our bodies are challenged when receiving a vaccine, "hitting the wall" while running a marathon, or even dealing with the initial shock of encountering ice-cold water in the shower. In contrast, it is difficult to employ physical resilience within lifelong stress, such as when it is prolonged within chronic disease, physical disability, or, more recently, physical complications related to exposure to COVID-19. Research surrounding the Yerkes-Dodson law (see Figure 8.1) describes the optimal range of stress as the midpoint between eustress (thriving) and distress (surviving).

TABLE 8.1 Thriving Versus Surviving				
	Cumulative load	**Predictability**	**Duration**	**Quality**
Characteristics of stress that make it optimal for achieving physical resilience	Micro	Predictable	Situational	Eustress
Characteristics of stress that make it difficult to achieve physical resilience	Macro	Unpredictable	Lifelong	Distress

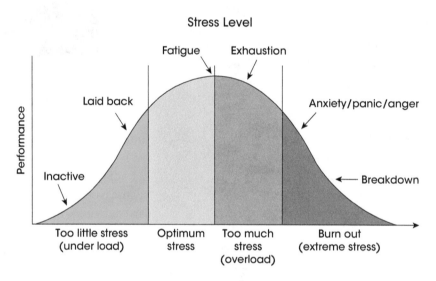

FIGURE 8.1   Yerkes-Dodson Law of Optimal Stress

EXERCISE 8.1: HOW DO YOU FACE ADVERSITY?

Reflect for a moment on the following question:

Think about a time when you have encountered adversity or stress in your life. How was the stress cumulative? Was it predictable? How long did the stress sustain its force?

Write down what you discovered.

Now again, reflect on the next question:

Think about a time when you had a close friend who encountered adversity or stress in their life. How was the stress cumulative? Was it predictable? How long did the stress sustain its force?

Write down what you discovered.

Finally, consider the difference between how you respond to adversity and how a close friend responds to adversity. Do you notice any patterns?

Write down what you discovered.

Healthspan Indicators

You have probably heard it before: "If you do not take care of your wellness, you will be required to take care of your illness." Understanding how adversity affects your healthspan, which is the number of years we remain healthy and free from diseases, is critical in how you regulate your optimal stress levels. While you do not always have control over the adversity you face, you do have control over how you respond to adversity. In a physical sense, you can control the values of your healthspan. These values include physiological reserve, nutrition, and recovery. Within these three values are measurable dimensions that further drive quality of life, or healthspan (see Table 8.2).

TABLE 8.2 Healthspan Dimension Values		
Physiological Reserve	Nutrition	Recovery
Cardiovascular endurance	Anthropometric body composition	Homeostasis
Musculoskeletal strength, range of motion	Biochemical nutrient absorption	Morbidity diagnosis, disease count, risk, and prognosis
	Clinical nutritional deficiency	
	Dietary caloric intake	

Physiological Reserve

Physiological reserve includes two measurable dimensions, cardiovascular and musculoskeletal. Cardiovascular assessment and interpretation can be completed through a physical cardiorespiratory endurance stress test, which measures submaximal or maximal volume of oxygen consumption your body can utilize during aerobic physical activity. In addition, heart rate variability (HRV) is an indicator of cardiovascular fitness. Musculoskeletal assessment and interpretation can be completed through a functional strength and flexibility test, which measures relative strength, absolute strength, repetition maximum estimation, and range of motion.

Nutrition

Nutrition includes four measurable dimensions, including anthropometric, biochemical, clinical, and dietary. The first, anthropometric assessment, is comprised of completing a low-dose radiation scan to measure size, weight, and proportions of the body. Known as body composition, this assessment tool measures bone density, visceral adipose tissue fat, and lean muscle mass. Assessment data can be interpreted to calculate fracture risk, metabolic health, and sarcopenia.

In biochemical assessment and interpretation, levels of nutrients in a person's blood, urine, or stools are assessed. Laboratory test results can be used to identify problems that may affect a person's appetite or nutritional status.

Nutritional clinical assessment involves checking for visible signs of physical nutritional deficiencies. It also consists of taking a medical history to identify comorbidities with nutritional implications, such as food and drug interactions and risk factors for disease (e.g., smoking, alcohol use, overweight).

Dietary assessment and interpretation involve checking food quantity and nutritional quality of intake as well as changes in appetite, food allergies and intolerance. Measures include 24-hour food recall, intake frequency, and macronutrient assessment. Individuals who complete these assessments benefit from counseling to improve their diets to prevent malnutrition or treat conditions affected by food intake and nutritional status.

Recovery

Recovery includes two measurable dimensions, homeostasis and morbidity. Homeostasis assessment and interpretation involves checking the body's vital signs, including blood pressure, core body temperature, heart rate, respiratory rate, oxygen saturation, metabolic panel, and heart rate variability (HRV). Morbidity assessment and interpretation involves checking for the presence or risk of disease and determining prognosis.

EXERCISE 8.2: HOW IS YOUR PHYSICAL HEALTH WORKING FOR YOU?

Reflect for a moment on the following question:

How do you feel when you receive objective feedback that your healthspan dimension values are outside average ranges (e.g., cardiovascular endurance, musculoskeletal strength and flexibility, body composition, energy levels, chronic disease risk and prognosis)?

Write down what you discovered.

Now again, reflect on the next question:

How do you feel when you're unable to optimally adapt to physical adversity (e.g., burnout, insomnia, lack of libido, chronic inflammation, or irritable bowel syndrome)?

Write down what you discovered.

Reflect on the next question:

How does it impact you when you fail at something you care about (e.g., fitting into your bathing suit, completing a walking or running challenge, or lifting a specific amount of weight)?

Write down what you discovered.

Finally, consider how assessing your current physical health will affect your longevity. What habit might you change to improve your physical resilience?

Write down what you discovered.

Conceptual Model of Physical Resilience and Systems

The force of adversity can have a cumulative effect on the body physically, and healthspan values require regular adjustment to maintain homeostasis. Therefore, it is important to design systems to become physically resilient. One system that has shown sustainable results is the practice of habits. In addition to optimal stress, sustainable habits are at the core of physical resilience. When you implement your habits at optimal stress loads, you create an acclimatized affect that results in adaptation to the trajectory of force. If the habit is positive, it leads to upward trajectory (growth), and alternatively, if the habit is negative, it leads to downward trajectory (decline). Your objective with physical resilience is to create positive habits that lead growth through functional recovery (see Figure 8.2).

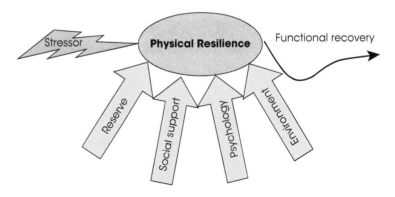

FIGURE 8.2   Conceptual Model of Physical Resilience

Faulty Systems and Physical Function

Maybe you have heard "You do not rise to the level of your goals, but instead you fall to the level of your systems." What do you really know when you say sustainable habits and optimal stress are at the core of resilience? We know habits repeat themselves to elicit change, both positively and negatively. Change occurs through the systems that are in place. For example, you can create systems to break bad habits just as well as you can create systems to create good habits.

Why? Because how you choose to respond drives your beliefs, processes, and outcomes for change. The direction in how you choose to approach change drives your system. For example, by starting with your beliefs, your process drives your outcomes, resulting in adaption or decline. Knowing how to design a system correctly is critical to achieving sustainable habits. Further, the theory of compounding contributes to the cumulative effect sustainability has. For example, the more you repeat the same behavior or habit, the greater its cumulative effect is on what you are changing. Therefore, to reach the ultimate objective through the practice of physical resilience, you must be very intentional in how you develop positive versus negative habits. Otherwise, you risk the chance of becoming vulnerable and fragile.

Given the unpredictable nature of virus transmission and mutation, such as with COVID-19, and the future uncertainty of other macrostressors that we encounter, building your capacity of physical resilience requires a critical pause to engage in a live autopsy of your body and assess its potential physical vulnerabilities. Doing such prevention practices not only begins to increase your levels of physical resilience to situational stress but also increases your ability to be physically resilient to your lifelong stress.

Systematic Approach to Physical Resilience

The remainder of this chapter focuses on a systematic approach to behavior change. It is essential to change behaviors through habit formation. This approach consists of three outlined steps: assessment and interpretation, habit design and implementation, and objective outcome evaluation.

Assessment and Interpretation

In the first step, you must obtain your dimensional healthspan values. This can be achieved by scheduling regular preventative physical health screenings with a primary care physician, exercise physiologist, registered dietician, or any other health specialist. Once obtained, interpretation of these assessment results is required to identify what dimensional healthspan values require attention.

Behavior Change Design and Implementation

The next step is to design and implement behavior change. Behavior change occurs best when designed from the direction of who you wish to become (beliefs) to what you hope to achieve (outcome; see Table 8.3).

TABLE 8.3 Direction of Behavior Change

	Activating Event	Belief	System	Outcome	Evaluation	New Physical State
Questions to ask	Identify encountered adversity	Ask yourself who you want to become	Ask yourself how you will respond	Ask yourself what you hope to accomplish	Ask yourself if the behavior change was worth it	You are now a ... You are an individual who ... You experience ...
Example	Suboptimal cardiovascular endurance	A healthy adult	Learn to run	Improved health (quality of life)	Absolutely	I am a healthy adult who runs to experience an improved quality of life.

EXERCISE 8.3: HOW CAN YOU APPLY THE DIRECTION OF BEHAVIOR CHANGE TO FURTHER DEVELOP YOUR PHYSICAL RESILIENCE?

Reflect for a moment on the following question:

Think for a moment about a situational type of physical adversity you have recently experienced. Now, ask yourself who you want to become because of experiencing this adversity (e.g., runner, deep sleeper, vegetarian).

Write down what you discovered.

Reflect on the next question:

Ask yourself how you will respond to adversity to change your habits (e.g., get 8 hours of sleep each night and eliminate screen time 2 hours before bedtime, move every hour, avoid processed foods and eat more fruits and vegetables).

Write down what you discovered.

Reflect on the next question:

Ask yourself what you hope to accomplish in the face of adversity (e.g., fitting into your bathing suit, completing a marathon, or lifting two times your weight).

Write down what you discovered.

Reflect on the final question:

Finally, reflect on your new physical state. Is this what you want for yourself? What have you achieved? How did you achieve it? Who have you become?

Write down what you discovered.

Habit Design

Once you know who you want to become, how you want to achieve it, and what you want to achieve, you can design your habit. Habit design consists of four laws. To create a positive habit (good) that increases your physical resilience, it requires making the habit obvious, attractive, easy, and satisfying. On the opposite end of the spectrum, to break a negative habit (bad) that increases your physical resilience, it requires making the habit invisible, unattractive, difficult, and unsatisfying. As you can see, there are two approaches to designing habits that can increase your physical resilience: addition of positive habits or elimination of negative habits (see Table 8.4). Research shows it is easier to build a positive habit than to break a negative habit.

TABLE 8.4 How to Create a Good Habit or Break a Bad Habit				
	1st Law	2nd Law	3rd Law	4th Law
	Cue	Craving	Response	Reward
Good (+) Habit	Obvious	Attractive	Easy	Satisfying
Bad (−) Habit	Invisible	Unattractive	Difficult	Unsatisfying

Once you have your habit designed and ready to implement, you may be asking what the magic is to implement your habit. By now, hopefully you have designed your habit to be so easy to implement that you cannot fail at the first step. Just do it. Treat it like a game and you do not want to lose against yourself. There is no magic; just start where you are and do not stop. If you miss a step, do not look back. Instead, fall forward.

Objective Outcome Evaluation

Now that you are completing your habit, you will need to periodically assess your progress. This can be best accomplished using a habit tracker. You can track habits daily, weekly, monthly, quarterly, annually, etc. By now you should have some momentum and objective data to evaluate what habits are working and what habits are not. This data can further evaluate the status of your dimensional healthspan values. It is important to remember that this is a journey. If you focus on the journey and not the destination, the habit will sustain. Think about who you want to become, how you want to achieve, and what you want to achieve. Answering these questions can be a powerful force in overcoming the face of adversity.

Physical Resilience and Longevity Strategies and Tactics

A list of strategies and tactics for developing physical resiliency

1. Regularly assess your physical health goals.
2. Write down and rate (+, −) your current habits to become aware of them.
3. Consider habit stacking to create momentum "After [current habit], I will [new habit]."
4. Be the architect of your physical environment.
5. Identify the habit(s) that have the greatest ripple effect.
6. Use a habit tracker.
7. Write down what you say you will do. "I will [action] at [time] in [location]."
8. Complete a habit contract with a trusted friend.
9. Time block your day to schedule in your habits.
10. Two-minute rule: scale the habit down until it only takes 2 minutes or less to perform.
11. Automate reminders to do habit.
12. Evaluate habit completion daily, weekly, monthly, quarterly, and annually.

13. Focus on creating positive habits first and breaking negative habits last.
14. Go slow, shaping the habit so tiny you cannot fail with an attempt.
15. Identify who you want to become, how you want to get there, and what you want to accomplish when you are 30, 40, 50, 60, … 90, etc.
16. Anticipate obstacles.
17. Focus on 1% improvement each day.
18. If not now, when?
19. Trust the process and enjoy the journey.
20. Take no days off.
21. Gamify the process.
22. Torch the complacency.
23. Take inventory to overcome what your excuses are for not challenging yourself physically and share it with someone.
24. Create an accountability mirror with Post-it Notes. List your insecurities, dreams, habits, and goals.
25. Write down what you do not like to do or what makes you uncomfortable. Then go do one of those things and do it again.
26. Push beyond your normal stopping point.

Summary

In summary, this chapter provided a knowledge source about the definition, conceptual model, benefits, and obstacles of physical resilience. In addition, a step-by-step road map was provided for you to learn the art of implementing physical resilience in your daily life situations. Using self-inventory and self-reflection after learning and applying the concepts and skills in this workbook, you are now able to develop step-by-step sustainable practices to increase your physical resilience, especially in unpredictable and uncertain times.

Reflection Questions

1. Knowing what you know now, what might you consider doing next to improve your physical resilience?
2. Apply the systematic approach to physical resilience to a physically adverse situation you wish to address. What is the activating event? Ask yourself who you wish to become because of this event. Ask yourself how you will respond because of this event. And finally, what do you hope to accomplish because of this event?
3. What can you do to improve your habits? The four laws for creating a good habit include making it obvious, attractive, easy, and satisfying. Take a moment to identify a habit you want to create. Using the four laws, shape your habit. Try it out and see what happens. Consider using any of the tips or strategies to enhance sticking to your habit. After tracking your habit, determine if you need to size down your habit.

References

Attia, P. (2017, January 22). *How you move defines how you live.* https://peterattiamd.com/move-defines-live/

———(2020, October 8). *Welcome.* https://peterattiamd.com/start-here/

Bernardes, R., & Baixinho, C. L. (2018). A physical resilience conceptual model—contributions to gerontological nursing. *Revista Brasileira De Enfermagem, 71*(5), 2589–2593. doi:10.1590/0034-7167-2017-0111

Chatterjee, R. (2019). *Stress solution: The 4 steps to reset your body, mind, relationships and purpose.* Penguin Books, Limited.

Clear, J. (2019). *Atomic habits: An easy and proven way to build good habits and break bad ones.* Avery Penguin Random House.

Ellin, A. (2020, December 17). *Special report: How resilience can get us through the pandemic.* Everyday Health. https://www.everyday-health.com/wellness/state-of-resilience/

Fetters K. A. (2020, September 12). *How you can tap into that elusive runner's high.* Runner's High. https://www.runnersworld.com/training/a20851505/how-to-achieve-a-runners-high/

Forlines, M. (2019, May 13). *Why is physical resilience important?.* https://marthaforlines.com/why-is-physical-resilience-important#:~:text=Physical%20resilience%20refers%20to%20the,healthy%20resting%20state%20following%20exertion.&text=Physical%20resilience%20is%20important%20for,order%20to%20effectively%20lead%20others.

GE Healthcare. (n.d.). *Lunar iDXA.* https://www.gehealthcare.com/products/bone-and-metabolic-health/lunar-idxa

Godin, S. (2020). *The practice: Shipping creative work.* Penguin Business.

Goggins, D. (2020). *Can't hurt me: Master your mind and defy the odds.* Lioncrest Publishing.

Hurley, K., Sood, A., Ellin, A., & Kilroy, D. (2020, December 11). *What is resilience? Definition, types, building resiliency, benefits, and resources.* Everyday Health. https://www.everydayhealth.com/wellness/resilience/#:~:text=Resilience%20is%20the%20ability%20to,%2C%20emotional%20upheaval%2C%20and%20suffering.&text=Resilient%20people%20tap%20into%20their,challenges%20and%20work%20through%20problems

Ilano, J. (2019, December 10). *Build resilience now: Help your body bend, not break, when things go wrong.* GMB Fitness. https://gmb.io/resilience/

Keeler, E. (2020, April 07). *A message from the chief wellness officer.* The Ohio State University College of Pharmacy. https://u.osu.edu/happyhealthyyou/2020/04/07/a-message-from-the-chief-wellness-officer-4/

Kurt, C. (2013, November 24). *Is "antifragile" better than "resilient"?* https://www.resilience.org/stories/2013-11-24/is-antifragile-better-than-resilient/

LeBrasseur, N. K. (2017). Physical resilience: Opportunities and challenges in translation. *The Journals of Gerontology. Series A, Biological Sciences and Medical Sciences, 72(7)*, 978–979. doi:10.1093/gerona/glx028

Linden, D. J. (n.d.). *The truth behind "runner's high" and other mental benefits of running.* Johns Hopkins Medicine. https://www.hopkinsmedicine.org/health/wellness-and-prevention/the-truth-behind-runners-high-and-other-mental-benefits-of-running

Linehan, M. (2015). *DBT® skills training handouts and worksheets.* The Guilford Press.

Loehr, J., & Groppel, J. (2008). *The corporate athlete advantage: The science of deepening engagement.* Human Performance Institute.

Mallory, A. (2018, June 21). *Physical resilience.* https://alanmallory.com/2018/06/physical-resilience/

Mathias, G. (2017, March 8). *How to develop physical resilience.* https://gillmathias.com/cultivate-physical-resilience/#:~:text=WHAT%20IS%20PHYSICAL%20RESILIENCE%3F,acutely%20damaged%20or%20microbially%20obesieged.

McGonigal, K. (2013). *The willpower instinct: How self-control works, why it matters, and what you can do to get more of it.* Avery Publishing Group.

———(2013, March 25). *Training for mind-body resilience: Research explores how exercise can protect against the harmful effects of chronic stress.* https://www.ideafit.com/personal-training/training-for-mind-body-resilience/

———(2021). *Joy of Movement: How exercise helps us find happiness, hope, connection, and courage.* Avery Publishing Group.

Mears, L. (2019, January 01). The science of stress. *Psychology Now, 1*, 62–67.

Melnyk, B. M. (2020, February 20). *10 ways to be more resilient in tough times.* https://www.osu.edu/alumni/news/ohio-state-alumni-magazine/issues/spring-2020/resilience-tips-nursing-ohio-state.html

Moore, M., Jackson, E., & Tschannen-Moran, B. (2016). *Coaching psychology manual.* Wolters Kluwer.

Neff, K., & Germer, C. (2018). *The mindful self-compassion workbook.* The Guilford Press.

Newport, C. (2020). *The time-block planner: A daily method of deep work in a distracted world.* Portfolio/Penguin.

Norton, E. O. (2017, February 27). *5 ways to build physical resilience* [Web log post]. http://www.areallybiglife.com/5-ways-build-physical-resilience/

O'Brien, P. (2020, July 28). *Here's how working out can make you more resilient to stress.* https://www.shape.com/fitness/tips/exercise-mental-resilience-stress

Pullen, W. (2017). *Running with mindfulness.* Penguin Random House.

Resnick, B., Galik, E., Dorsey, S., Scheve, A., & Gutkin, S. (2011). Reliability and validity testing of the physical resilience measure. *The Gerontologist, 51*(5), 643–652. doi:doi.org/10.1093/geront/gnr016

Riopel, L. (2020, September 19). *Resilience skills, factors and strategies of the resilient person.* https://positivepsychology.com/resilience-skills/

Robertson, S. (2020, January 9). *Antifragile is the new resilient.* https://thriveglobal.com/stories/antifragile-is-the-new-resilient/#:~:text=Author%2C%20scholar%2C%20former%20trader%20and,that%20is%20in%20constant%20flux.

Saremi, S. (2017, November 6). *Mindful running: 5 questions with author Mackenzie L. Havey.* https://www.runwalktalk.com/blog/mindful-running-interview

Schorr, A., Carter, C., & Ladiges, W. (2018). The potential use of physical resilience to predict healthy aging. *Pathobiology of Aging & Age-Related Diseases, 8*(1), 1–3. doi:0.1080/20010001.2017.1403844

Sholl, J., Spayde, J., Staff, E., & Gelb, M. (2020, December 01). *The 5 best ways to build resiliency.* Experience Life. https://experiencelife.com/article/the-5-best-ways-to-build-resiliency/

Sood, A., & Melnyk, B. M. (2020, April 04). *Discover the resilient you: Strengthen your self-confidence and self-control—the two top skills to bounce back from any situation.* https://images.agoramedia.com/everydayhealth/gcms/Everyday-Health-Resilience-Workbook.pdf?slot=2&eh_uid=54149119&utm_source=Newsletters&nl_key=nl_resilience_welcome_series&utm_content=2020-04-04&utm_campaign=Resilience_Welcome_Series

Sphancer, N. (2020, October). Designed for success. *Psychology Today,* 45–53.

Starrett, K., & Cordoza, G. (2015). *Becoming a supple leopard: The ultimate guide to resolving pain, preventing injury, and optimizing athletic performance.* Victory Belt Publishing.

Trainsmart Wellness. (2019, March 18). *Building resilience: How to improve your body's physical resilience to stress.* https://trainsmart-wellness.ca/blog/building-resilience-how-to-improve-your-bodys-physical-resilience-to-stress/

Whitson, H. E., Duan-Porter, W., Schmader, K. E., Morey, M. C., Cohen, H. J., & Colón-Emeric, C. S. (2015). Physical resilience in older adults: Systematic review and development of an emerging construct. *The Journals of Gerontology Series A: Biological Sciences and Medical Sciences, 71*(4), 489–495. doi:10.1093/gerona/glv202

Willyerd, K., & Mistick, B. (2016). *Stretch: How to future-proof yourself for tomorrow's workplace.* John Wiley & Sons.

Yaeger, D. (2011). *Greatness: The 16 characteristics of true champions.* Center Street.

Credits

Conclusion

Congratulations on reaching the end of this book on resilience. Whether you took in the whole book or simply skimmed the content, you can become more aware of options you might choose to take toward living a more healthy life. The emphasis here is on discovering your options rather than prescribing what "you should do." This is because each of us has individual preferences, and what seems important to one may not be important to the other.

After reading this text, watch out for concluding, "I should have known." You were always doing the best you knew how in living your life. However, most of what we deem as normal is the result of learned habits from our parents or peers. Many of those habits are helpful, such as brushing your teeth in the morning. You do not have to research peer-reviewed literature to brush your teeth, even though it might be possible to take another approach to oral health. Other habits, like negative self-talk, are also learned over time, but they can be harmful to your ability to live well. These habits need to be carefully examined, as many are just old stories from growing up that no longer apply to our lives. For example, learning to placate a difficult parent teaches that 1) you should respond to unreasonable or bullying demands and 2) you are somehow responsible for the emotional response of that difficult parent. The habits we grew up with include what we eat, whom we prefer to affiliate with, and many other habits.

As we recognize that most habits are simply stories we learned earlier in life, we can view the habits in a more compassionate light. Most of those habits were adaptive and helped us navigate relationships with parents and the world and represent our younger self's best conclusions regarding how to respond. Children learn these habits very quickly, as it can be a matter of survival. On the other hand, some innocuous comments from parents can be internalized almost instantly. I had one client who was confused about their difficulties in relationships. Over the course of therapy, that person identified that when they were 6 years old, they gravitated to the clothes associated with the other biological gender. The person's mother made a comment about that being inappropriate, and this person internalized that with the story "I can never let people see who I really am." This realization allowed this person to challenge the story of needing to hide and made it safer to explore concerns related to gender identity and sexual preference.

Viewing changes as correcting old habits is preferable to judging yourself as "bad" because you discover a better way to respond to challenges in your life. It is fine to judge the habit as helpful or harmful, but you are not that habit. For example, if I smoke cigarettes, that is a very harmful habit, but smoking does not make me a bad person. When I recognize the habit as harmful (health implications, expense for cigarettes, etc.), I am free to make changes if I desire. Recognize that just because a habit is harmful, it will take extra energy to engage and change the habit. In my mental health practice, I have suggested to a few clients that the current moment was not the right time to try and quit smoking because that person had too many other stressors in the moment, and asking the person to "do more" right then was not practical.

Please adopt a compassionate style of relating to yourself. The habit you may wish to address served a younger version of yourself and was the best that you could figure out in that moment. Beating yourself up only makes that inner child more afraid and more likely to hide. You want to enlist that younger version of yourself as a resource for better understanding how current habits/stories came to be. You need that information as you decide which habits to change and when to change them.

Reflection Questions

1. Take 10–15 minutes starting with meditation as described earlier in this book. After your body feels calmer (perhaps 5 minutes into the meditation), ask yourself "What changes do I wish to make based on this book?"

Simply wait for a bit to see what bubbles up. Sometimes we may conclude a desire to start on a particular problem, and sometimes we may wish to have more time to consider our options.

2.   See if there are two or three items from this book that you want to address. In identifying those items, you have started the contemplation phase, as noted in Prochaska's stages of change. Allow yourself to put together a plan of action (including discussing your ideas with peers or mentors as you deem helpful).

3.   As best you can, put away shame for what is past. Being human means making mistakes, as mistakes are how we learn. Shame blocks us from further exploration of a problem. Can you identify one or two areas you feel ashamed about and reflect on whether you can forgive yourself and let go of the feeling of shame?

Index

About the Editors

Paul F. Granello is an associate professor of counselor education at The Ohio State University. He is also in private practice at Well Counselors Inc. in Worthington, Ohio. Paul is interested in wellness, resiliency, stress, and many other topics. He has received more than $2 million in grant funding for suicide prevention research. He has developed a curriculum that has been approved by the State of Ohio Board of Colleges and Schools to train counselors and social workers to be certified wellness counselors.

Matt Fleming is a graduate of The Ohio State University (MA in counselor education and MSEE) and Ohio Northern University (BSEE). Matt interned as a counselor trainee at OSU Counseling and Consultation Service, worked there for 2 years as a fellow, and continued for 3 more years as a senior staff member. He set up and ran a private counseling practice until retiring in 2019. Prior to pursuing a career in the counseling field, Matt worked for 25 years as an engineer and project manager. At the Battelle Memorial Institute, he was recognized as an eminent inventor, receiving 15 patents in the areas of medical products and information security. While enjoying retirement, Matt continues to work part-time as a life coach/consultant and is spending more time outdoors.

About the Contributors

Dr. Ana C. Berríos Allison is a licensed professional counselor in the state of Ohio. Her experience in higher education includes career counseling, individual and group counseling, grief and loss, and adjunct teaching in the counselor education programs of The Ohio State University and University of Dayton. Her counseling interests relate to the influences of contextual factors and family dynamics in career decision-making, career and wellness, career transitions, and spirituality as well as multicultural counseling. Ana has published and presented at numerous conferences, nationally and internationally, about career counseling and social justice among various clients and special populations. Dr. Berríos Allison served on the board of the Ohio Career Development Association (OCDA) and has been recognized at the state level as the recipient of many leadership and counseling awards, including the Ohio Counseling Association (OCA) Charles "Chuck" Weaver Award. Additionally, Ana volunteers at the OSU James Care for Life, co-facilitating career counseling groups for cancer survivors and Latinx patients. She is a certified spiritual director who provides spiritual companionship in the community.

Lindsey Carelli is the Associate Director for Interfaith Initiatives at Stetson University. She directs interfaith programming, supports religious and nonreligious student organizations, and works with the university chaplains to advance spiritual awareness at Stetson. Additionally, she facilitates educational and experiential opportunities to engage students and community members in contemplative practices, such as dialogue, meditation, and yoga. Lindsey holds a Master of Theological Studies degree from Brite Divinity School in Fort Worth, Texas, and a BA in Religious Studies from the University of Oklahoma.

Tim Graham, MA, LPC, CHWC, has a private counseling and coaching practice focusing on preventive wellness interventions in the areas of career, cognitive, emotional, nutritional, and physical health in Columbus, Ohio. Tim is an endurance athlete who has competed in more than a dozen marathons, ascended two of the top four tallest mountain summits in the contiguous United States, and is a two-time finisher of the Ironman triathlon. A former full-time higher education professional turned wellness advocate, Tim is a husband, father of two, and an inspiration to others as a transformative example of courageous and healthy living. Tim has supported students at The Ohio State University through academic, athletic, career, cognitive, emotional, physical, and social wellness and is a licensed professional counselor (LPC) and certified health and wellness coach (CHWC). Tim earned his MA in counselor education, clinical mental health from The Ohio State University and holds additional degrees in sport and exercise management (MA) and education (BSEd). Tim is licensed in Ohio (C.1902348). His website is www.centralohiowellnesscounseling.com.

Tyler Hudson is a licensed professional counselor and a certified wellness counselor working in private practice in Columbus, Ohio. He holds a master's degree in mental health counseling and a master's degree in theological studies. Tyler is also a PhD candidate at The Ohio State University, where he researches wellness, men's mental health, and suicide prevention. He lives in Delaware, Ohio, with his wife and two sons.

Mark E. Young is Professor Emeritus at the University of Central Florida. He is the author of five textbooks, including the widely used *Learning the Art of Helping*. For more than 20 years, he worked as a counselor, including 6 years in college counseling centers. He is past president of the Association for Spiritual, Ethical and Religious Values in Counseling and has been a meditator for more than 50 years.

Brett Zyromski is an assistant professor at The Ohio State University. His scholarship focuses on the impact of evidence-based interventions in school counseling, evidence-based school counselor education, and evaluation in school counseling. He currently serves as an associate editor for the *Professional School Counseling* journal. In addition to evidence-based school counseling, Dr. Zyromski's scholarship also explores how school counseling programs remove barriers to success for all students, with special attention paid to how school counselors can enhance protective factors and positive childhood experiences for students who have experienced adverse childhood experiences.

Dr. Zyromski is the co-founder and co-chair of the national Evidence-Based School Counseling Conference (http://www.ebscc.org) and has published over 25 peer-reviewed articles and book chapters related to school counseling issues, has delivered over 85 international, national, regional, and local presentations, and has served as keynote speaker at numerous international and state conferences. He is co-author of *Facilitating Evidence-Based, Data-Driven School Counseling: A Manual for Practice* (Corwin, 2016). Dr. Zyromski is also involved with the American School Counselor Association (ASCA) as a Lead Recognized-ASCA-Model-Program Reviewer (LRRs) and has also served as a trainer of the ASCA National Model for the American School Counselor Association. He has successfully helped over two dozen schools successfully earn RAMP. Dr. Zyromski has served as project manager for $5,541,223 worth of federal and state grants.

CPSIA information can be obtained
at www.ICGtesting.com
Printed in the USA
LVHW012028310822
727261LV00007B/328